CORRECTIVE SPELLING THROUGH
MORPHOGRAPHS

STUDENT'S BOOK

ROBERT DIXON
SIEGFRIED ENGELMANN

SCIENCE RESEARCH ASSOCIATES, INC.
Chicago, Henley-on-Thames, Sydney, Toronto
A Maxwell Pergamon Publishing Company

be

ICE be
ICE
ICE be
ICE
ICE be IC
ICE
ICE be DI inter IC hood
ICE DI inter ship IC hood
r ICE DI ship IC hood
r at ICE be DI inter ship IC hood
r at ICE ly for DI inter ship IC hood
r at ICE ly be for DI ship IC ag hood
r at ICE ly for DI inter ship IC ag hood
r at ICE ly be for DI inter ship IC ag hood com
r at ICE ly be for DI inter ship IC ag hood com
r at ICE ly for DI TRANS ship IC ag hood com
r at ICE ly be for DI TRANS inter ship IC ag hood com
r at ICE ly for est TRANS inter ship IC ag hood com
r at ICE ly be for est DI TRANS inter ship IC ag hood com
r at ICE ly for est DI TRANS inter ship IC ag hood com
r at ICE ly be for est DI TRANS inter ship IC ag hood com
r at ICE ly for est DI TRANS inter ship IC ag hood com
r at ICE ly be for est DI TRANS inter ship IC ag hood com
r at ICE ly for est DI TRANS ship IC ag hood com
r at ICE ly be for est DI TRANS inter ship IC ag hood com

ISBN 0-574-08852-0

Part A

1. _____ ring
2. _____ ringing
3. _____ wondering
4. _____ wonder
5. _____ renting
6. _____ react
7. _____ watering
8. _____ repacking

Part B

1. _____
2. _____
3. _____
4. _____
5. _____
6. _____

Part C

1. _____
2. _____
3. _____
4. _____

Part D

1. _____ + _____ = wondering
2. _____ + _____ + _____ = repacking
3. _____ + _____ = reborn
4. _____ + _____ = spending

PART	A	B	C	D	E	F	G	H	Worksheet Errors	Worksheet Points	Oral Points	Bonus Points	Total Points
											+	+	=

Lesson 2

Part A

1. _____ resting
2. _____ rest
3. _____ string
4. _____ reborn
5. _____ quieting
6. _____ stringing
7. _____ refreshing
8. _____ watering

Part B

1. _____
2. _____
3. _____

Part C

1. _____
2. _____
3. _____
4. _____
5. _____
6. _____

Part D

1. _____
2. _____
3. _____
4. _____
5. _____
6. _____

Part E

1. _____ + _____ + _____ = relighting
2. _____ + _____ = brushing
3. _____ + _____ = refresh
4. _____ + _____ = crashing

PART	A	B	C	D	E	F	G	H	Worksheet Errors	Worksheet Points	Oral Points	Bonus Points	Total Points
											+	+	=

Part A

1. _____ refresh
2. _____ resting
3. _____ rest
4. _____ rent

5. _____ refreshing
6. _____ wondering
7. _____ ringing
8. _____ ring

Part B

1. _____
2. _____

3. _____
4. _____

Part C

1. _____
2. _____
3. _____
4. _____

5. _____
6. _____
7. _____
8. _____

Part D

1. _____ + _____ = wondering
2. _____ + _____ + _____ = repacking
3. _____ + _____ = spending
4. _____ + _____ + _____ = unpacking

Part E

Circle the words in the lines.

1. (quiet) quietqueitquitequietpuietqnietquiettquiet
2. (light) ligthlightlligtlitelightlightlightllightlitgh
3. (refresh) refershrefreshrefersrefershrefrcshrefresherefresh
4. (wondering) wonduringwwonderingwonderinwonderinggwondering

PART	A	B	C	D	E	F	G	H	Worksheet Errors	Worksheet Points	Oral Points	Bonus Points	Total Points
											+	+	=

Lesson 4

Part A

1. _____ fun
2. _____ unborn
3. _____ fresh
4. _____ refreshing
5. _____ unrefreshing
6. _____ rerent

Part B

Draw a line from each morphograph to its meaning.

re •   • when you do something

ing •   • the most

un •   • again

est •   • not

Part C

1. _____

2. _____

3. _____

Part D

1. _____

2. _____

3. _____

4. _____

5. _____

6. _____

Part E

1. _____ + _____ = unpack

2. _____ + _____ = report

3. _____ + _____ + _____ = resorting

4. _____ + _____ = lightest

Part F

1. (thickest)   thickestthickistthicknessthickestthickestthickset

2. (unpack)   unpaekunpackununpakeunpackuunpackunupackunpack

3. (rematch)   remachremacthrematchcrematchrematcrematch

4. (reporting) ereportinreportingrreportingreprotingreporting

PART	A	B	C	D	E	F	G	H	Worksheet Errors	Worksheet Points	Oral Points	Bonus Points	Total Points
											+	+	=

4

Part A

1. _____
2. _____
3. _____
4. _____

5. _____
6. _____
7. _____

Part B

1. _____
2. _____

3. _____
4. _____

Part C

Draw a line from each morphograph to its meaning.

re •   • when you do something

ing •   • the most

est •   • again

un •   • not

Part D

1. _____ + _____ + _____ = reporting
2. _____ + _____ = unhappy
3. _____ + _____ = quieting
4. _____ + _____ = respell
5. _____ + _____ = lighting
6. _____ + _____ = resort

Lesson 5

Part E

Circle the words in the lines.

1. (refreshing)   refresingrefershingrefreshingreefreshing

2. (light)   ligthlighttlitelightlitghlightlightlifth

3. (quietest)   quietestqueitestqueitistquietestpuietest

4. (match)   machmatchnatchmatchmmatchnatshmatshmatch

Bonus Exercise

1. **quiet**   qui __ t qu __ __ t q __ __ __ __ t __ __ __ __ __ __

2. **match**   mat __ h ma __ __ h ma __ __ __ __ m __ __ __ __ h __ __ __ __ __ __

3. **thick**   thic __ thi __ __ th __ __ __ t __ __ __ __ __ __ __ __ __ __ __

4. **brush**   br __ sh br __ __ h b __ __ __ __ h __ __ __ __ __ h __ __ __ __ __ __

5. **light**   lig __ t li __ __ t li __ __ __ l __ __ __ __ __ __ __ __ __ __ __

6. **fresh**   f __ esh f __ __ sh f __ __ __ h __ __ __ __ __ h __ __ __ __ __ __

PART	A	B	C	D	E	F	G	H	Worksheet Errors	Worksheet Points	Oral Points	Bonus Points	Total Points
											+	+	=

6

Part A

1. _____
2. _____

3. _____
4. _____

Part B

1. _____
2. _____
3. _____
4. _____

5. _____
6. _____
7. _____
8. _____

Part C

1. _____
2. _____
3. _____

4. _____
5. _____
6. _____

Part D

Draw a line from each morphograph to its meaning.

est   •   • when you do something

re   •   • without

un   •   • the most

ing   •   • again

less   •   • not

Part E

1. _____ + _____ = helpless

2. _____ + _____ + _____ = unpacking

3. _____ + _____ = motoring

4. _____ + _____ = matchless

5. _____ + _____ + _____ = resorting

7

Lesson 6

Part F

Circle the words in the lines

1. (author)   autherauthorathorautherauthorauauthoranther
2. (matchless)   matchlesmatchlessmacthlessmatchlessmatcmatchless
3. (motor)   motormotromotermotorrmotormoturmctormotor
4. (brush)   drushburshbruchbrushbrurshdrushbrushbrbrush

Bonus Exercise

1. **author**	auth ___ r	aut ___ ___ ___	au ___ ___ ___ ___	a ___ ___ ___ ___ ___
2. **light**	l ___ ght	l ___ ___ ht	l ___ ___ ___ t	l ___ ___ ___ ___ ___ ___ ___ ___
3. **spend**	sp ___ nd	sp ___ ___ d	s ___ ___ ___ d	___ ___ ___ ___ d ___ ___ ___ ___
4. **quiet**	qui ___ t	qu ___ ___ t	q ___ ___ ___ t	___ ___ ___ ___ t ___ ___ ___ ___
5. **wonder**	won ___ ___ r	w ___ n ___ ___ ___	w ___ ___ ___ ___ ___	___ ___ ___ ___ ___
6. **motor**	m ___ tor	m ___ ___ or	m ___ ___ ___ r	___ ___ ___ ___ r ___ ___ ___ ___

PART	A	B	C	D	E	F	G	H	Worksheet Errors	Worksheet Points	Oral Points	Bonus Points	Total Points
											+	+	=

Part A

1. _____ 3. _____

2. _____ 4. _____

Part B

b u h o t e i n c

a f r u s g i m o

Part C

1. _____ 3. _____

2. _____ 4. _____

Part D

Figure out each word and write it in the blank below.

huanppy   aothru

1. _____ 2. _____

amcht   rerefsh

3. _____ 4. _____

Part E

Draw a line from each morphograph to its meaning.

mis •   • not

re •   • when you do something

less •   • wrong

un •   • the most

ing •   • again

est •   • without

Part F

Fill in the blanks to show the morphographs in each word.

1. _____ + _____ + _____ = misspending

2. _____ + _____ = grandest

3. _____ + _____ = matchless

4. _____ + _____ + _____ = refreshing

5. _____ + _____ = friendless

6. _____ + _____ + _____ = misspelling

PART	A	B	C	D	E	F	G	H	Worksheet Errors	Worksheet Points	Oral Points	Bonus Points	Total Points
											+	+	=

Lesson 8

Part A

1. _____ 3. _____

2. _____ 4. _____

Part B

n e c j k o v d l

p a r f u e i o t

Part C

1. _____ 4. _____

2. _____ 5. _____

3. _____ 6. _____

Part D

Figure out each word and write it in the blank below.

endfri   mssiepll   shestfre

1. _____ 2. _____ 3. _____

wingdoner   mastike

4. _____ 5. _____

Part E

Fill in the blanks to show the morphographs in each word.

1. _____ + _____ = unhuman

2. _____ + _____ = stretching

3. _____ + _____ + _____ = unfilling

4. _____ + _____ + _____ = mismatching

5. _____ + _____ = thickest

6. _____ + _____ = helpless

10

Part F

Draw a line from each morphograph to its meaning.

mis •   • not

est •   • again

ing •   • the most

un •   • without

less •   • wrong

re •   • when you do something

Part G

Circle the word in the lines.

1. (stretch)   stretchstretchstretchstretchstertchstretchststretch

2. (human)   humenhumanhnuanhumanhuhumannnumanhumanhumahhuman

3. (friend)   freindfriendffriendfirendfriendfrendfriendfrienfriend

4. (authoring) authorauthoringautheringsauthoringangauthoring

PART	A	B	C	D	E	F	G	H	Worksheet Errors	Worksheet Points	Oral Points	Bonus Points	Total Points
										+	+	=	

11

Lesson 9

Part A

1. _____   2. _____

Part B

1. _____   4. _____
2. _____   5. _____
3. _____

Part C

b   e   i   r   t   u   l   o   p

a   c   v   n   i   k   j   t   u

Part D

1. _____   3. _____
2. _____   4. _____

Part E

Figure out each word and write it in the blank below.

sterhct   ingcrsha   othuar

1. _____   2. _____   3. _____

munha   fienrd   lghitste

4. _____   5. _____   6. _____

Part F

Draw a line from each morphograph to its meaning.

un •
mis •
ing •
less •
est •
re •
ness •

• when you do something
• that which is
• not
• without
• wrong
• the most
• again

Part G

Circle the words in the lines.

1. (pressing)   pressignpressingpresspressingperssingpressingingpress
2. (unpack)   unpaeknupackunupackunpacknubackunbackunpackpack
3. (stretch)   stertchstretchsrstrcthstretcstretcnstretchstertch
4. (lightest)   litghestlightlightistlightestligthestlightestlilightesl

PART	A	B	C	D	E	F	G	H	Worksheet Errors	Worksheet Points	Oral Points	Bonus Points	Total Points
											+	+	=

Lesson 10

Part A

1. _____   5. _____

2. _____   6. _____

3. _____   7. _____

4. _____   8. _____

Part B

a   c   i   m   s   u   d   o   p

v   e   o   u   n   t   z   r   k

Part C

1. _____   3. _____

2. _____   4. _____

Part D

Write each of these words in a box.

Write "free space" in one box.

stretch	thickest	misspelling	report	helpless
unhappy	dullest	dullness	friendly	define
author	matchless	crashing	right	catcher

PART	A	B	C	D	E	F	G	H	Worksheet Errors	Worksheet Points	Oral Points	Bonus Points	Total Points
											+	+	=

Part A

1. _____   5. _____

2. _____   6. _____

3. _____   7. _____

4. _____

Part B

Write each of these words in a box.

Write "free space" in one box.

stretching	refreshing	helpless	quietness	mismatch
take	misspend	brushing	backless	freshness
refillable	repacking	unborn	thickness	motor

Part C

b   r   e   n   o   p   z   i   a   g   u   k   i   e

Part D

Figure out each word and write it in the blank below.

heplnseslses   preress   itstrcheng

1. _____   2. _____   3. _____

drienf   kate   smellisp

4. _____   5. _____   6. _____

Lesson 11

Part E

Draw a line from each morphograph to its meaning.

un •   • again

est •   • when you do something

ness •   • not

less •   • able to be

re •   • the most

ing •   • wrong

able •   • that which is

mis •   • without

Part F

Circle the words in the lines.

1. (author)   anthorauthauthorrauthorauothorauthoraautnorauthor

2. (mismatch)   mismatcmismatshmismatchmismatmismatchmismacth

3. (quietest)   queitestquietistquietquietestqnietestquietest

4. (misspell)   mispelllmisspelmisspellmisspelmispelmisspellmispel

Bonus Exercise

1. **stretch**   str ___ tch   st ___ ___ tch   st ___ ___ ___ ch   s ___ ___ ___ ___ ___ ___

2. **quiet**   qui ___ t   qu ___ ___ t   q ___ ___ ___ t   ___ ___ ___ ___ t   ___ ___ ___ ___ ___

3. **thick**   th ___ ck   th ___ ___ k   t ___ ___ ___ k   t ___ ___ ___ ___   ___ ___ ___ ___ ___

4. **spending**   sp ___ nd ___ ___ g   sp ___ ___ ___ ___ ng   s ___ ___ ___ ___ ___ ___ g

PART	A	B	C	D	E	F	G	H	Worksheet Errors	Worksheet Points	Oral Points	Bonus Points	Total Points
											+	+	=

16

Part A

1. Kit was _____ about the _____.

2. I'm going to _____ out and enjoy a good tennis _____.

Part B

1. _____   3. _____

2. _____

Part C

Write the word for each meaning.

	word	meaning
1.	_____	that which is thick
2.	_____	able to be stretched
3.	_____	when you press
4.	_____	spell wrong
5.	_____	not born
6.	_____	the most grand
7.	_____	without help

Part D

Make a little **v** above every vowel letter.

Make a little **c** above every consonant letter.

u   b   n   i   o   k   l   a   e   q   t   i   h   a

Lesson 12

Part E

Draw a line from each morphograph to its meaning.

able   •   • without

ness   •   • able to be

ing   •   • that which is

less   •   • when you do something

Part F

Figure out each word and write it in the blank below.

    ssepr   fnierd

1. _____   2. _____

    serort   ghtil

3. _____   4. _____

Part G

Circle the word in each line.

1. (portable)   portalbeportableprotableportebleportablepoportalbe

2. (misspend)   mispendmisspnedmisspendmismisspendmissendmisspend

3. (author)   authorautheranthorauthauthorawthosauthoraauthor

4. (humanness)   humanesshumannesshumaneshunamnesshumannesshumaness

PART	A	B	C	D	E	F	G	H	Worksheet Errors	Worksheet Points	Oral Points	Bonus Points	Total Points
											+	+	=

18

Part A

1. _____   3. _____

2. _____   4. _____

Part B

1. The _____ being was not _____ .

2. An _____ and his _____ are _____ on crime.

Part C

Write the word for each meaning.

word	**meaning**
1. _____	name again
2. _____	that which is grand
3. _____	able to be stretched
4. _____	not like
5. _____	without match

Part D

Figure out each word and write it in the blank below.

drewon   tchestr   ifne

1. _____   2. _____   3. _____

Bonus Exercise

1. **human**   hum___n   hu___ ___n   h___ ___ ___n   ___ ___ ___ ___n   ___ ___ ___ ___ ___

2. **author**   a___thor   a___ ___ ___or   a___ ___ ___ ___r   ___ ___ ___ ___ ___ ___

3. **light**   lig___t   li___ ___t   l___ ___ ___t   ___ ___ ___ ___t   ___ ___ ___ ___ ___

4. **stretch**   stre___ch   stre___ ___ ___   str___ ___ ___ ___   ___ ___ ___ ___ ___ ___ ___

PART	A	B	C	D	E	F	G	H	Worksheet Errors	Worksheet Points	Oral Points	Bonus Points	Total Points
											+	+	=

19

Lesson 15

Part A

1. _____   4. _____
2. _____   5. _____
3. _____   6. _____

Part B

1. like + able   = _____
2. match + less   = _____
3. like + ness   = _____
4. help + ing   = _____
5. dine + ing   = _____

6. human + ness   = _____
7. use + able   = _____
8. use + ful   = _____
9. wide + est   = _____
10. face + ing   = _____

Part C

1. _____   3. _____
2. _____   4. _____

Part D

Draw a line from each morphograph to its meaning.

un   •   • without
est   •   • not
ness •   • that which is
less •   • again
re   •   • the most
able •   • when you do something
ing   •   • wrong
mis   •   • able to be
ed   •   • in the past

Part E

Write the word for each meaning.

	word	meaning
1.	_____	help in the past
2.	_____	fill again
3.	_____	spell wrong
4.	_____	the most grand
5.	_____	without hope

PART	A	B	C	D	E	F	G	H	Worksheet Errors	Worksheet Points	Oral Points	Bonus Points	Total Points
											+	+	=

Part A

1. _____
2. _____
3. _____

4. _____
5. _____

Part B

1. use + less   = _____
2. friend + less   = _____
3. care + ing   = _____
4. stretch + able   = _____
5. dine + ed   = _____
6. quiet + ed   = _____

7. bare + ness   = _____
8. note + able   = _____
9. note + ing   = _____
10. author + ing   = _____
11. take + ing   = _____
12. care + less   = _____

Part C

Write each of these words in a box.

Write "free space" in one box.

grade	quietness	use	wide	wondered
refine	night	hope	lightest	thickest
misspelling	right	humanness	dullness	stretchable

Lesson 16

Part D

Figure out each word and write it in the blank below.

ghtir   rothau   lefirl

1. _____   2. _____   3. _____

Part E

Circle the words in the lines.

1. (night)   nightrightnigthinighthginightniphtnight

2. (stretching)   stretchingstretchingstrecthingstretchingstretching

3. (use)   uzeuseususeuuseaseuseseuseyouuse

Bonus Exercise

1. **right**   ri ___ ht   r ___ ___ ht   r ___ ___ ___ t   ___ ___ ___ ___ t   ___ ___ ___ ___ ___

2. **serve**   serv ___   ser ___ ___   se ___ ___ ___   s ___ ___ ___ ___   ___ ___ ___ ___ ___

3. **hope**   ho ___ e   h ___ ___ e   h ___ ___ ___   ___ ___ ___ ___   ___ ___ ___ ___

4. **human**   h ___ man   h ___ ___ an   h ___ ___ ___ n   ___ ___ ___ ___ n   ___ ___ ___ ___ ___

PART	A	B	C	D	E	F	G	H	Worksheet Errors	Worksheet Points	Oral Points	Bonus Points	Total Points
											+	+	=

22

Part A

1. _____
2. _____
3. _____

4. _____
5. _____
6. _____

Part B

1. dine + ing   = _____
2. wide + ness   = _____
3. catch + able = _____
4. serve + ing   = _____
5. trace + ing   = _____
6. motor + ing   = _____
7. bare + ed   = _____

8. name + less   = _____
9. name + ing   = _____
10. like + able = _____
11. like + ness = _____
12. dull + est   = _____
13. dull + ness = _____
14. care + ing   = _____

Part C

1. _____
2. _____
3. _____
4. _____
5. _____
6. _____
7. _____
8. _____

Part D

Draw a line from each morphograph to its meaning.

re •	• wrong
ing •	• in the past
un •	• before
est •	• when you do something
less •	• the most
mis •	• able to be
ness •	• not
able •	• without
ed •	• again
pre •	• that which is

PART	A	B	C	D	E	F	G	H	Worksheet Errors	Worksheet Points	Oral Points	Bonus Points	Total Points
											+	+	=

Lesson 18

Part A

1. Toronto is a large and beautiful _____ .

2. Before the tennis _____ , we did _____ exercises.

3. Janie _____ a marble from her _____ .

4. The waiter will _____ a _____ lunch.

5. Our _____ during the holiday was pure _____ .

Part B

1. snap   3. sad   5. wander   7. sell

2. face   4. shop   6. catch   8. shop

Part C

1. _____ + _____ = _____

2. _____ + _____ = _____

3. _____ + _____ = _____

4. _____ + _____ = _____

5. _____ + _____ = _____

6. _____ + _____ = _____

7. _____ + _____ = _____

8. _____ + _____ = _____

Part D

These words are in the puzzle.

Circle 7 or more of the words.

author   human   sad   thick

grand   name   lock   handed

ate   stretch   wide   help

```
h  a  t  l  w  i  d  e
a  u  t  h  o  r  r  h
n  a  m  e  i  c  c  e
d  k  s  a  d  c  k  l
e  g  r  a  n  d  k  p
d  s  t  r  e  t  c  h
```

Part E

Write the word for each meaning.

	word	meaning
1.	_____	one who helps
2.	_____	pack before
3.	_____	fill in the past
4.	_____	more fresh
5.	_____	stretch before
6.	_____	that which is grand
7.	_____	use wrong
8.	_____	when you stretch

Part F

Circle the words in the lines.

1. servesrveservesserveseverservesreve

2. tracetratracetrasetarcetracettraceetrace

PART	A	B	C	D	E	F	G	H	Worksheet Errors	Worksheet Points	Oral Points	Bonus Points	Total Points
											+	+	=

Lesson 19

Part A

1. _____   4. _____

2. _____   5. _____

3. _____   6. _____

Part B

1. swim   4. step   7. motor

2. grade   5. arm   8. thick

3. water   6. shop   9. plan

Part C

1. _____ + _____ = _____

2. _____ + _____ = _____

3. _____ + _____ = _____

4. _____ + _____ = _____

5. _____ + _____ = _____

6. _____ + _____ = _____

Part D

These words are in the puzzle.

Circle 7 or more of the words.

right	night	light	late
than	trace	like	friend
that	note	author	grade

t r n t g h t

r l i g h t n

a i g g t a o

c k h r h t t

e e t l a t e

f r i e n d e

a u t h o r e

26

Part E

Draw a line from each morphograph to its meaning.

pre   •   • that which is

ed   •   • able to be

er   •   • without

able   •   • one who, more

ness   •   • the most

less   •   • in the past

est   •   • again

re   •   • before

Part F

Figure out each word and write in in the blank below.

inght   entc   dagre

1. _____   2. _____   3. _____

Bonus Exercise

1. **right**   r ___ ght   r ___ ___ ht   r ___ ___ ___ t   ___ ___ ___ ___ t   ___ ___ ___ ___ ___

2. **serve**   serv ___   ser ___ ___   se ___ ___ ___   s ___ ___ ___ ___   ___ ___ ___ ___ ___

3. **human**   hum ___ n   hu ___ ___ n   h ___ ___ ___ n   ___ ___ ___ ___ n   ___ ___ ___ ___ ___

4. **friend**   frien ___   frie ___ ___   fri ___ ___ ___   fr ___ ___ ___ ___   ___ ___ ___ ___ ___

5. **match**   m ___ tch   m ___ ___ ch   m ___ ___ ___ h   ___ ___ ___ ___ h   ___ ___ ___ ___ ___

6. **quiet**   qu ___ et   qu ___ ___ t   q ___ ___ ___ t   q ___ ___ ___ ___   ___ ___ ___ ___ ___

PART	A	B	C	D	E	F	G	H	Worksheet Errors	Worksheet Points	Oral Points	Bonus Points	Total Points
											+	+	=

Lesson 20

Part A

1. _____
2. _____
3. _____

4. _____
5. _____
6. _____

Part B

1. _____
2. _____
3. _____
4. _____

5. _____
6. _____
7. _____
8. _____

Part C

1. _____ + _____ = _____
2. _____ + _____ = _____
3. _____ + _____ = _____
4. _____ + _____ = _____
5. _____ + _____ = _____
6. _____ + _____ = _____
7. _____ + _____ = _____
8. _____ + _____ = _____

Part D

Look at the last three letters of each word. Make a **v** or **c** above each of the last three letters.

Circle each short word that ends **cvc**. Remember, short words have four letters or less.

1. pen

2. press

3. red

4. wrap

5. brother

6. wide

7. drop

8. brush

9. stop

28

Part E

These words are in the puzzle.

Circle 7 or more of the words.

spell	fresh	light	friend
real	spend	seed	wide
said	name	grade	lone

```
n  s  p  e  l  l
s  a  p  f  l  l
f  w  m  e  o  g
f  r  i  e  n  d
s  e  e  d  e  d
l  a  i  s  e  l
l  l  i  g  h  t
g  r  a  d  e  t
```

Part F

Draw a line from each morphograph to its meaning.

ly   •   • more, one who

er   •   • before

pre •   • that which is

ed   •   • not

un   •   • how you do something

ness •   • in the past

ing •   • how something is

PART	A	B	C	D	E	F	G	H	Worksheet Errors	Worksheet Points	Oral Points	Bonus Points	Total Points
											+	+	=

Lesson 21

Part A

1. If your answers are _____ , you'll get a good _____ .

2. The _____ sold his goods in the _____ .

3. Martin _____ _____ portions of ice cream to his guests.

4. My _____ became tired from _____ out that _____ .

5. Our ship will sail into _____ at noon.

Part B

1. _____   5. _____

2. _____   6. _____

3. _____   7. _____

4. _____

Part C

Add these morphographs together. Some of the words follow the rule about dropping an **e**.

1. like + ness = _____

2. fine + est   = _____

3. name + ly   = _____

4. note + ing   = _____

5. note + able = _____

6. grade + ing = _____

7. wide + er   = _____

8. hope + ing   = _____

9. use + ed   = _____

10. dine + ing   = _____

11. serve + ed   = _____

12. care + less = _____

13. bare + ed   = _____

14. trace + ing = _____

15. face + less = _____

16. hate + ing   = _____

Look at the last three letters of each word. Make a **v** or **c** above each of the last three letters.

Circle each short word that ends **cvc**. Remember, short words have four letters or less.

1. plan   4. big   7. clan

2. rest   5. step   8. drop

3. arm   6. brother

Part E

Draw a line from each morphograph to its meaning.

ed •   • not

pre •   • before

er •   • without

ly •   • in the past

ness •   • when you do something

ing •   • more, one who

un •   • the most

less •   • that which is

est •   • how something is

PART	A	B	C	D	E	F	G	H	Worksheet Errors	Worksheet Points	Oral Points	Bonus Points	Total Points
											+	+	=

31

Lesson 22

Part A

Add these morphographs together. Some of the words follow the rule about dropping an **e.**

1. note + able = _____

2. like + ing = _____

3. fine + er = _____

4. fine + ness = _____

5. fine + ly = _____

6. hope + less = _____

7. use + less = _____

8. use + ing = _____

9. trace + ing = _____

10. bare + ly = _____

11. wide + ness = _____

12. wide + ly = _____

13. wide + est = _____

14. serve + ing = _____

15. like + able = _____

Part B

Fill in the blanks to show the morphographs in each word.

1. _____ + _____ + _____ = helplessness

2. _____ + _____ = reserve

3. _____ + _____ = humanness

4. _____ + _____ = quietly

5. _____ + _____ + _____ = resorting

6. _____ + _____ = formless

7. _____ + _____ = friendly

8. _____ + _____ = stretcher

9. _____ + _____ + _____ = unpacked

10. _____ + _____ + _____ = unmatchable

Part C

Write the word for each meaning.

	word	meaning
1.	_____	that which is thick
2.	_____	press before
3.	_____	able to spend
4.	_____	name wrong
5.	_____	stretch in the past
6.	_____	without a friend
7.	_____	not happy
8.	_____	the most fresh

32

Part D

These words are in the puzzle.

Circle 7 or more of the words.

speller	serve	spend
city	press	part
hear	deal	care
rake	have	grade

```
s  s  s  d  p  s  g
s  p  p  e  a  h  r
p  h  e  a  r  a  a
c  c  n  l  t  v  d
i  a  d  l  l  e  e
t  r  r  a  k  e  e
y  p  r  e  s  s  r
```

Part E

1. (trace)   trasetarcetraceetetracelracetracetatraceetrace
2. (equal)   equalequallequalegualequaleauglequalegual

PART	A	B	C	D	E	F	G	H	Worksheet Errors	Worksheet Points	Oral Points	Bonus Points	Total Points
											+	+	=

33

Lesson 24

Part A

1. _____
2. _____
3. _____

4. _____
5. _____
6. _____

Part B

1. _____ + _____ = tracing
2. _____ + _____ = careless
3. _____ + _____ = faced
4. _____ + _____ = notable
5. _____ + _____ = named
6. _____ + _____ = barely

Part C

Add these morphographs together. Some of the words follow the rule about dropping an **e.**

1. care + ing   = _____
2. cart + ed   = _____
3. hate + ing   = _____
4. mis + take + ing = _____
5. un + friend + ly = _____
6. bare + ly   = _____
7. note + able   = _____
8. wide + ly   = _____

Part D

Draw a line from each morphograph to its meaning.

ness •   • one who, more

ly •   • that which is

un •   • how something is

able •   • not

mis •   • able to be

est •   • wrong

re •   • the most

er •   • again

Part E

Figure out each word and write it in the blank below.

lequa   rvesse

1. _____   3. _____

ticy

2. _____

PART	A	B	C	D	E	F	G	H	Worksheet Errors	Worksheet Points	Oral Points	Bonus Points	Total Points
											+	+	=

DOUBLE WHEN CVC + V

Part A

1. _____
2. _____
3. _____

4. _____
5. _____

Part B

1. run + er   = _____
2. water + ed   = _____
3. sad + ness   = _____
4. help + ful   = _____

5. swim + ing   = _____
6. mad + ly   = _____
7. form + less = _____
8. sad + er   = _____

Part C

Write the word for each meaning.

word	meaning
1. _____	full of help
2. _____	away from the port
3. _____	how something is equal
4. _____	one who helps
5. _____	more fresh
6. _____	wash before
7. _____	that which is grand
8. _____	when you stretch

Part D

Add these morphographs together. Some of the words follow the rule about dropping an **e**.

1. face + less   = _____

2. de + note + ing   = _____

3. mis + use + ing   = _____

4. re + fine + able   = _____

5. pre + serve + ing = _____

6. force + ful   = _____

7. choice + est   = _____

8. care + less   = _____

Part E

Fill in the blanks to show the morphographs in each word.

1. _____ + _____ = serving

2. _____ + _____ = diner

3. _____ + _____ = wideness

4. _____ + _____ = hoping

5. _____ + _____ = hopeless

6. _____ + _____ = useful

PART	A	B	C	D	E	F	G	H	Worksheet Errors	Worksheet Points	Oral Points	Bonus Points	Total Points
											+	+	=

DOUBLE WHEN CVC + C

Part A

1. I _____ to _____ in mountain lakes.

2. The _____ of this book rewrote every _____.

3. A shark is _____ against the side of its _____ .

4. Maria was _____ because she had to _____ a picture.

5. Pierre's _____ _____ when he was twelve years old.

Part B

1. bar + ed   = _____   6. wander + ed = _____

2. arm + ing   = _____   7. pack + ing   = _____

3. snap + ing   = _____   8. wash + able = _____

4. mad + ness = _____   9. shop + ing   = _____

5. plan + ed   = _____   10. run + er   = _____

Part C

1. _____   4. _____

2. _____   5. _____

3. _____   6. _____

Part D

1. _____ + _____ = _____

2. _____ + _____ = _____

3. _____ + _____ = _____

4. _____ + _____ = _____

5. _____ + _____ = _____

6. _____ + _____ = _____

7. _____ + _____ = _____

Part E

Draw a line from each morphograph to its meaning.

ful •   • away from

de •   • without

est •   • able to be

ly •   • full

ness •   • the most

er •   • again

pre •   • how something is

re •   • before

less •   • more, one who

able •   • that which is

Part F

These words are in the puzzle.

Circle 7 or more of the words.

change   voice   cage   knee

choice   sink   hope   cape

force   shop   bar   sad

```
c  v  v  v  b  s  f
h  c  s  o  o  a  o
s  h  h  c  i  d  r
s  o  o  a  i  c  c
h  i  i  p  n  a  e
o  c  n  e  e  g  e
p  e  p  k  n  e  e
```

PART	A	B	C	D	E	F	G	H	Worksheet Errors	Worksheet Points	Oral Points	Bonus Points	Total Points
											+	+	=

DOUBLE WHEN CVC + V

Part A

1. _____   4. _____

2. _____   5. _____

3. _____   6. _____

Part B

1. stop + ing   =   _____   6. bliss + ful   =   _____

2. bar + ing   =   _____   7. snap + ing   =   _____

3. form + er   =   _____   8. arm + less   =   _____

4. sad + ness   =   _____   9. brother + ly   =   _____

5. plan + ed   =   _____   10. sad + en   =   _____

Part C

1. serve
   happy
   catcher
   frend

   _____

2. quiet
   equil
   thickness
   light

   _____

3. graid
   change
   watering
   preserve

   _____

4. human
   author
   strech
   trace

   _____

5. brush
   liht
   farm
   force

   _____

6. choise
   rage
   unhappy
   refreshing

   _____

Part D

Write the word for each meaning.

	word	meaning
1.	_____	to make light
2..	_____	full of hope
3.	_____	press away from
4.	_____	without hope

Part E

Add these morphographs together. Some of the words follow the rule about dropping an **e**.

1. de + face + ing   = _____

2. change + ing   = _____

3. help + ful + ness = _____

4. care+ful+ly   = _____

5. re + serve + ing   = _____

6. note + able   = _____

Part F

Fill inthe blanks to show the morphographs in each word.

1. _____ + _____ + _____ = reserving

2. _____ + _____ + _____ = reported

3. _____ + _____ + _____ = forcefully

4. _____ + _____ + _____ = restlessness

5. _____ + _____ = blissful

6. _____ + _____ = stretcher

7. _____ + _____ + _____ = reformed

8. _____ + _____ + _____ = unequally

PART	A	B	C	D	E	F	G	H	Worksheet Errors	Worksheet Points	Oral Points	Bonus Points	Total Points
											+	+	=

41

Lesson 28

Part A

1. _____   4. _____

2. _____   5. _____

3. _____   6. _____

Part B

1. stop + ing = _____   6. mad + ness = _____

2. shop + less = _____   7. bar + ed   = _____

3. shop + ing = _____   8. sad + ly   = _____

4. sell + er   = _____   9. wander + ed = _____

5. swim + er   = _____   10. quiet + ly = _____

Part C

1.	face	2.	awthor	3.	spelling
	rename		freshness		stretch
	trase		equal		author
	friendly		motor		happey
	_____		_____		_____

4.	change	5.	bliss	6.	page
	sirve		force		chanje
	trace		preserve		stretcher
	resort		moter		match
	_____		_____		_____

Part D

Draw a line from the morphographs to their meanings.

ness •   • before

en   •   • more, one who

ful   •   • to make

de   •   • how something is

ly   •   • in the past

er   •   • that which is

pre   •   • away from

ed   •   • full of

Part E

Add these morphographs together. Some of the words follow the rule about dropping an **e**.

1. take + en = _____

2. rage + ed = _____

3. re + coil + ing = _____

4. un + change + ed = _____

5. pre + plan = _____

6. de + press + ing = _____

7. sad + en = _____

8. mad + ness = _____

9. arm + ing = _____

Part F

Fill in the blanks to show the morphographs in each word.

1. _____ + _____ = really

2. _____ + _____ = passage

3. _____ + _____ = passing

4. _____ + _____ + _____ = unarmed

5. _____ + _____ + _____ = unchanged

6. _____ + _____ + _____ = hopefully

PART	A	B	C	D	E	F	G	H	Worksheet Errors	Worksheet Points	Oral Points	Bonus Points	Total Points
											+	+	=

Lesson 29

Part A

1. _____ 4. _____
2. _____ 5. _____
3. _____ 6. _____

Part B

Add these morphographs together. Some of the words follow the rule about doubling the final **c** in short words.

1. stop + ed   = _____ 6. grand + ly   = _____
2. cart + ing = _____ 7. sad + en   = _____
3. hot + ly   = _____ 8. mad + ness = _____
4. plan + er   = _____ 9. arm + ing   = _____
5. hot + est   = _____ 10. big + ger = _____

Part C

less	care	rest	ed	ful	ing	hope

1. _____ 7. _____
2. _____ 8. _____
3. _____ 9. _____
4. _____ 10. _____
5. _____ 11. _____
6. _____

Part D

These words are in the puzzle.

Circle 7 or more of the words.

strength   stretch   swim

hate   rest   mash   sack

rent   best   wash   hot   catch

```
s h o t m s b c
s t r c h a e h
w a r e s t s t
s t r e n g t h
w a s h t t s a
i i c a t c h t
m m i k s s h e
```

44

Part E

1. (strength)   strengthstregthstrengthstrenghstrength
2. (stretch)   stretchstretchstrechstretchhstretch

Bonus Exercise

1. **change**   cha ___ ge   cha ___ ___ e   ch ___ ___ ___ ___   ___ ___ ___ ___ ___ ___
2. **choice**   ch ___ ___ ce   ___ ___ ___ ___ ___ ce   ___ ___ ___ ___ ___ e   ___ ___ ___ ___ ___ ___
3. **equal**   equ ___ l   equ ___ ___   eq ___ ___ ___   e ___ ___ ___ ___   ___ ___ ___ ___ ___

PART	A	B	C	D	E	F	G	H	Worksheet Errors	Worksheet Points	Oral Points	Bonus Points	Total Points
											+	+	=

Lesson 30

Part A

1. _____
2. _____
3. _____

4. _____
5. _____

Part B

like	able	ing	stretch	note	ed	use

1. _____
2. _____
3. _____
4. _____
5. _____
6. _____

7. _____
8. _____
9. _____
10. _____
11. _____

Part C

1. _____
2. _____
3. _____

4. _____
5. _____
6. _____

Part D

Add these morphographs together.

Some of the words follow the rule about doubling the final **c** in a short word.

1. water + ing = _____
2. big + est   = _____
3. run + er   = _____
4. sad + ly   = _____
5. farm + ing = _____

6. want + ed = _____
7. sad + est = _____
8. dull + ness = _____
9. snap + ing = _____
10. plan + ed = _____

46

Part E

Circle the mispelled word in each group.

Then write it correctly in the blank.

1. stretch
   strength
   wandor
   force

   _____

2. length
   choyce
   change
   equal

   _____

3. human
   stregth
   trace
   bliss

   _____

Bonus Exercise

1. **strength**   stre ___ gth   stre ___ ___th   stre ___ ___ ___ ___   ___ ___ ___ ___ ___ ___ ___ ___
2. **stretch**   str ___ tch   str ___ ___ ch   str ___ ___ ___ ___   ___ ___ ___ ___ ___ ___ ___
3. **wander**   w ___ nder   w ___ ___ der   w ___ ___ ___ ___ r   ___ ___ ___ ___ ___ ___
4. **length**   le ___ gth   le ___ ___ th   l ___ ___ ___ th   ___ ___ ___ ___ th   ___ ___ ___ ___ ___ ___

PART	A	B	C	D	E	F	G	H	Worksheet Errors	Worksheet Points	Oral Points	Bonus Points	Total Points
											+	+	=

Lesson 31

Part A

1. _____ + _____ = _____
2. _____ + _____ = _____
3. _____ + _____ = _____
4. _____ + _____ = _____
5. _____ + _____ = _____
6. _____ + _____ = _____

Part B

Make 11 real words from the morphographs in the box.

fine	wide	ly	est	bare	quiet	ness

1. _____
2. _____
3. _____
4. _____
5. _____
6. _____

7. _____
8. _____
9. _____
10. _____
11. _____

Part C

Write the word for each meaning.

	word	**meaning**
1.	_____	to make dark
2.	_____	that which is dark
3.	_____	the most dark
4.	_____	away from the port
5.	_____	without help
6.	_____	full of help

Part D

Draw a line from the morphographs to their meanings.

ly •   • able to be

pre •   • more, one who

er •   • to make

ed •   • how something is

able •   • before

en •   • in the past

Part E

Look at the last three letters of each word. Make a **v** or **c** above each of the last three letters. Circle each short word that ends **cvc**.

1. hot   3. clan   5. world   7. fill

2. author   4. sign   6. swim   8. snap

Part F

Fill in the blanks to show the morphographs in each word.

1. _____ + _____ = used

2. _____ + _____ + _____ = strengthening

3. _____ + _____ + _____ = prestretched

4. _____ + _____ = hoping

5. _____ + _____ + _____ = unchanged

6. _____ + _____ = shining

PART	A	B	C	D	E	F	G	H	Worksheet Errors	Worksheet Points	Oral Points	Bonus Points	Total Points
											+	+	=

Lesson 32

Part A

1. _____
2. _____
3. _____

4. _____
5. _____

Part B

1. _____ + _____ = _____
2. _____ + _____ = _____
3. _____ + _____ = _____
4. _____ + _____ = _____
5. _____ + _____ = _____
6. _____ + _____ = _____
7. _____ + _____ = _____
8. _____ + _____ = _____

Part C

1. _____ + _____ = lonely
2. _____ + _____ = swimmer
3. _____ + _____ = noted
4. _____ + _____ = grading
5. _____ + _____ = snapper
6. _____ + _____ = madness

50

Part D

Make 13 real words from the morphographs in the box.

| like | wide | en | ing | ness | length | take | ly |

1. _____   8. _____

2. _____   9. _____

3. _____   10. _____

4. _____   11. _____

5. _____   12. _____

6. _____   13. _____

7. _____

Part E

Circle the misspelled word in each group. Then write it correctly in the blank.

1.	forse	2.	trace	3.	friend	4.	grade
	serve		change		auther		night
	stretch		voise		real		strength
	human		length		wander		civel

_____   _____   _____   _____

PART	A	B	C	D	E	F	G	H	Worksheet Errors	Worksheet Points	Oral Points	Bonus Points	Total Points
											+	+	=

51

Lesson 34

DOUBLE WHEN CVC + V

Part A

1. Mr. Nelson _____ the _____ over his _____ .

2. One _____ is _____ for a _____ storm.

3. Tony has tremendous _____ in her _____ _____ .

Part B

Write each of these words in a box. Write "free space" in one box.

| equal | play | night | dropper | blissful | unchanged | stretch |

| voice | berry | length | tracing | nerve | civil | humanly | wander |

Part C

Add these morphographs together. Some of the words follow the rule about dropping an **e.**

1. rage + ing   = _____   6. herb + al   = _____

2. race + er   = _____   7. lose + er   = _____

3. force + ful   = _____   8. like + en   = _____

4. change + less = _____   9. shine + ing   = _____

5. change + ing   = _____   10. page + less = _____

Part D

Add these morphographs together. Some of the words follow the rule about doubling the final **c** in a short word.

1. sad + ness = _____   5. big + est   = _____

2. run + less   = _____   6. snap + less = _____

3. run + ing   = _____   7. bar + ing   = _____

4. stop + er   = _____   8. mad + ly   = _____

PART	A	B	C	D	E	F	G	H	Worksheet Errors	Worksheet Points	Oral Points	Bonus Points	Total Points
											+	+	=

DOUBLE WHEN CVC + V

Part A

1. _____

   _____

2. _____

   _____

Part B

Add these morphographs together. Some of the words follow the rule about doubling the final **c** in short words.

1. hot + est   = _____

2. clan + ish   = _____

3. step + ing   = _____

4. mad + ness = _____

5. sad + er   = _____

6. water + ing = _____

7. stretch + er = _____

8. plan + ed   = _____

9. form + ed   = _____

10. snap + ed   = _____

Part C

These words are in the puzzle.

Circle 7 or more of the words.

serving	sell	arm
lone	port	vote
plan	voice	equal
game	sign	berry

```
s  g  i  s  i  g  n
s  e  r  v  i  n  g
b  q  l  p  o  o  a
e  u  v  l  o  t  m
r  a  o  a  a  r  e
r  l  o  n  e  r  t
y  v  o  i  c  e  m
```

Lesson 35

Part D

Write the word for each meaning.

The words will contain these morphographs:

ish - like   **de** - away from, down

al - related to   **ful** - full of

en - to make   **pre** - before

	word	**meaning**
1.	_____	full of hope
2.	_____	to make wide
3.	_____	press down
4.	_____	like a child
5.	_____	plan before
6.	_____	related to rent

Part E

Figure out each word and write it in the blank below.

1. shwa   2. rreby   3. iiclv   4. adwnre

_____   _____   _____   _____

Part F

Fill in the blanks to show the morphographs in each word.

1. _____ + _____ + _____ = playfully
2. _____ + _____ + _____ = designer
3. _____ + _____ = noting
4. _____ + _____ = notable
5. _____ + _____ + _____ = reserved
6. _____ + _____ + _____ = preplanned

PART	A	B	C	D	E	F	G	H	Worksheet Errors	Worksheet Points	Oral Points	Bonus Points	Total Points
											+	+	=

54

Part A

1. _____ 4. _____

2. _____ 5. _____

3. _____ 6. _____

Part B

1. _____ + _____ = _____

2. _____ + _____ = _____

3. _____ + _____ = _____

4. _____ + _____ = _____

5. _____ + _____ = _____

6. _____ + _____ = _____

Part C

Fill in the blanks to show the morphographs in each word.

1. _____ + _____ = shopping

2. _____ + _____ = widely

3. _____ + _____ = hopeless

4. _____ + _____ = hoping

5. _____ + _____ = runner

6. _____ + _____ = cared

Part D

Make 11 real words from the morphographs in the box.

ed	er	rent	bare	ing	serve	dine

1. _____ 7. _____

2. _____ 8. _____

3. _____ 9. _____

4. _____ 10. _____

5. _____ 11. _____

6. _____

PART	A	B	C	D	E	F	G	H	Worksheet Errors	Worksheet Points	Oral Points	Bonus Points	Total Points
											+	+	=

CONSONANT−Y + ANYTHING, EXCEPT I

Part A

1. _____   4. _____

2. _____   5. _____

3. _____

Part B

1. study + ed   = _____   4. study + ing   = _____

2. nasty + ness = _____   5. deal + er   = _____

3. boy + ish   = _____   6. happy + ness = _____

Part C

Make 15 real words from the morphographs in the box.

hope	use	ful	less	ly	care	rest

1. _____   9. _____

2. _____   10. _____

3. _____   11. _____

4. _____   12. _____

5. _____   13. _____

6. _____   14. _____

7. _____   15. _____

8. _____

Part D

Add these morphographs together. Some of the words follow the rule about doubling the final **c** in a short word.

1. big + est   = _____
2. mis + deal + ing = _____
3. sad + en   = _____
4. swim + er   = _____

5. run + ing   = _____
6. mad + ness   = _____
7. length + en   = _____
8. form + al +ly   = _____

Part E

Fill in the blanks to show the morphographs in each word.

1. _____ + _____ = biggest
2. _____ + _____ = planner
3. _____ + _____ = changing
4. _____ + _____ = dining
5. _____ + _____ = careful
5. _____ + _____ = barred
7. _____ + _____ = package
8. _____ + _____ = clannish

PART	A	B	C	D	E	F	G	H	Worksheet Errors	Worksheet Points	Oral Points	Bonus Points	Total Points
											+	+	=

Lesson 38

CONSONANT – Y + ANYTHING, EXCEPT I

Part A

1. _____   4. _____

2. _____   5. _____

3. _____

Part B

1. sturdy + ness = _____   4. fancy + ful = _____

2. dry + ing   = _____   5. play + ful = _____

3. note + ed   = _____   6. hurry + ing = _____

Part C

Make 15 real words from the morphographs in the box.

de	er	fine	serve	light	ing	grade

1. _____   9. _____

2. _____   10. _____

3. _____   11. _____

4. _____   12. _____

5. _____   13. _____

6. _____   14. _____

7. _____   15. _____

8. _____

Part D

Add these morphographs together. Some of the words follow the rule about doubling the final **c** in short words.

1. drop + ing = _____   5. bar + ing   = _____

2. plan + ing = _____   6. shop + less = _____

3. length + en = _____   7. hot + er   = _____

4. wash + er   = _____   8. step + ed   = _____

PART	A	B	C	D	E	F	G	H	Worksheet Errors	Worksheet Points	Oral Points	Bonus Points	Total Points
											+	+	=

CONSONANT – Y + ANYTHING, EXCEPT I

Part A

1. _____   5. _____
2. _____   6. _____
3. _____   7. _____
4. _____   8. _____

Part B

Add the morphographs together. Some of the words follow the rule about changing the **y** to **i** in a word.

1. boy + ish = _____
2. sturdy + er = _____
3. cry + er = _____
4. dry + est = _____
5. form + ing = _____
6. copy + ed = _____

Part C

		s or es		**plural word**
1. press	+	_____	=	_____
2. shop	+	_____	=	_____
3. buzz	+	_____	=	_____
4. stretch	+	_____	=	_____
5. form	+	_____	=	_____
6. deal	+	_____	=	_____

Lesson 39

Part D

Make 11 real words from the morphographs in the box.

Some of the words follow the rule about doubling the final **c** in short words.

s	ed	snap	rest	shop	step	ing

1. _____   7. _____

2. _____   8. _____

3. _____   9. _____

4. _____   10. _____

5. _____   11. _____

6. _____

Part E

Fill in the blanks to show the morphographs in each word.

1. _____ + _____ = buzzer

2. _____ + _____ = civilly

3. _____ + _____ = dropper

4. _____ + _____ = strengthen

5. _____ + _____ = really

6. _____ + _____ + _____ = informer

PART	A	B	C	D	E	F	G	H	Worksheet Errors	Worksheet Points	Oral Points	Bonus Points	Total Points
											+	+	=

Part A

1. _____   4. _____

2. _____   5. _____

3. _____

Part B

Write **s** or **es** in the second column. Then add the morphographs together.

	s or es	plural word
1. back	+ _____	= _____
2. match	+ _____	= _____
3. wash	+ _____	= _____
4. crash	+ _____	= _____

Part C

Add the morphographs together. Some of the words follow the rule about changing **y** to **i** in a word.

1. joy + ful = _____   5. worry + ing = _____

2. pity + ful = _____   6. worry + er = _____

3. dry + er = _____   7. cry + ing = _____

4. human + ness = _____   8. play + er = _____

Part D

1. _____

_____

2. _____

_____

Part E

Make 11 real words from the morphographs in the box.

er	ly	est	ness	mad	thick	sad

1. _____   7. _____

2. _____   8. _____

3. _____   9. _____

4. _____   10. _____

5. _____   11. _____

6. _____

Lesson 40

Part F

Write the word for each meaning. The words will contain these morphographs.

ish - like   **con** - with   **in** - in, not   **de** - down, away

al - related to   **age** - related to   **en** - to make   **ful** - full of

	word	**meaning**
1.	_____	related to form
2.	_____	sign with
3.	_____	take in
4.	_____	to make fresh
5.	_____	away from port
6.	_____	related to something packed
7.	_____	like a fool
8.	_____	full of use

PART	A	B	C	D	E	F	G	H	Worksheet Errors	Worksheet Points	Oral Points	Bonus Points	Total Points
											+	+	=

Part A

1. _____   4. _____
2. _____   5. _____
3. _____   6. _____

Part B

Add the morphographs together. Some of the words follow the rule about changing **y** to **i** in a word.

1. study + ed = _____   5. water + ed = _____
2. study + ing = _____   6. sturdy + ness = _____
3. fancy + ful = _____   7. worry + er = _____
4. cry + er = _____   8. nasty + ness = _____

Part C

Write **s** or **es** in the second column. Then add the morphographs together.

	s or es	**plural word**
1. box	+ _____	= _____
2. buzz	+ _____	= _____
3. snap	+ _____	= _____
4. stretch	+ _____	= _____

Part D

Circle the misspelled word in each group. Then write it correctly in the blank.

1. world
   civel
   shining
   wander

   _____

2. happy
   motor
   auther
   friend

   _____

3. stretch
   choice
   herb
   forse

   _____

4. equil
   change
   hopeful
   trace

   _____

5. depressing
   realy
   humanness
   wrong

   _____

6. should
   would
   could
   nasti

   _____

63

Lesson 41

Part E

Make 11 real words from the morphographs in the box.

stretch	stop	wash	snap	er	ed	ing

1. _____   7. _____
2. _____   8. _____
3. _____   9. _____
4. _____   10. _____
5. _____   11. _____
6. _____

Part F

Circle the words in the line.

1. (strength)   strenthstrengthstrethstrengthhstrengthstrestrength
2. (stretch)   stretchstrestretchstrechstretchchstretchsstretch
3. (friend)   frindfriendfrendfrienddfriendfreindfrienddfriend
4. (sturdy)   studysturdysterdysturdyyststurdysturdsturdyssturdy
5. (worry)   woryworrywerryworryywworryworworryworyworrywworry
6. (sign)   signnsnsignsingsignsinesignsingsignnsignnsign

PART	A	B	C	D	E	F	G	H	Worksheet Errors	Worksheet Points	Oral Points	Bonus Points	Total Points
											+	+	=

Part A

1. _____
2. _____
3. _____

4. _____
5. _____
6. _____

Part B

1. _____
2. _____
3. _____
4. _____

5. _____
6. _____
7. _____
8. _____

Part C

Make 5 real words from the morphographs in the box.

age	use	pack	ing	er

1. _____
2. _____
3. _____
4. _____
5. _____

Part D

Add the morphographs together. Some of the words follow the rule about changing **y** to **i** in a word.

1. baby + ish = _____
2. play + er = _____
3. try + ing = _____
4. hurry + ed = _____

5. dry + ly = _____
6. busy + ly = _____
7. buzz + er = _____
8. copy + er = _____

Lesson 42

Part E

Write **s** or **es** in the second column. Then add the morphographs together.

	s or **es**	**plural word**
1. crash	+ _____	= _____
2. fox	+ _____	= _____
3. buzz	+ _____	= _____
4. sign	+ _____	= _____

Part F

Draw a line from the homonyms to their meanings.

homonym   **meaning**

right •   • doing something correctly

write •   • putting words on paper

PART	A	B	C	D	E	F	G	H	Worksheet Errors	Worksheet Points	Oral Points	Bonus Points	Total Points
											+	+	=

Part A

1. _____   5. _____
2. _____   6. _____
3. _____   7. _____
4. _____

Part B

1. _____ + _____ = _____
2. _____ + _____ = _____
3. _____ + _____ = _____
4. _____ + _____ = _____
5. _____ + _____ = _____
6. _____ + _____ = _____
7. _____ + _____ = _____
8. _____ + _____ = _____

Part C

Make 7 real words from the morphographs in the box.

| pack   age   bag   ed   ing |

1. _____   5. _____
2. _____   6. _____
3. _____   7. _____
4. _____

Part D

Figure out each word and write it in the blank below.

thengstr   rreby   tiwre   throme

1. _____ 2. _____ 3. _____ 4. _____

Lesson 43

Part E

Write **s** or **es** in the second column. Then add the morphographs together.

	s or **es**	**plural word**

1. light + _____ = _____

2. tax + _____ = _____

3. buzz + _____ = _____

4. press + _____ = _____

5. run + _____ = _____

6. box + _____ = _____

7. brush + _____ = _____

8. catch + _____ = _____

Part F

Fill in the blanks to show the morphographs in each word.

1. _____ + _____ + _____ = conserving

2. _____ + _____ = biggest

3. _____ + _____ = wrapper

4. _____ + _____ = lately

5. _____ + _____ = shining

6. _____ + _____ + _____ = unchanging

7. _____ + _____ + _____ = rerunning

8. _____ + _____ = loser

PART	A	B	C	D	E	F	G	H	Worksheet Errors	Worksheet Points	Oral Points	Bonus Points	Total Points
											+	+	=

Part A

Figure out the rule and write it. Remember to spell the words correctly.

and the next morphograph begins with **v** . . .when the word ends **cvc** . . .Double the final **c** in a short word

_____

_____

Part B

1. _____

_____

2. _____

_____

Part C

1. brother	2. rong	3. shineing
story	wrap	hurried
shuld	nasty	joyful
were	civil	wander
_____	_____	_____

4. stretch	5. swimer	6. stretcher
civilly	runner	friendly
realy	berry	unarmmed
unfilling	restful	shopper
_____	_____	_____

Lesson 44

Part D

Add the morphographs together. Some of the words follow the rule about dropping an **e**.

1. write + ing   = _____
2. safe + ly   = _____
3. late + er   = _____
4. lone + ly   = _____
5. force + ful   = _____
6. like + able   = _____
7. re + serve + ing = _____
8. note + able   = _____
9. change + ing   = _____
10. wide + ly   = _____

Part E.

Circle each short word that ends **cvc.**

• Remember : The letter **x** acts like two consonant letters.

stop   mad   rent   box   boy   plan

brother   play   hot   clan   water

fox   buzz   bar   bare   snap

PART	A	B	C	D	E	F	G	H	Worksheet Errors	Worksheet Points	Oral Points	Bonus Points	Total Points
											+	+	=

Part A

Figure out the rules and write them. Remember to spell the words correctly.

1. a word when the next morphograph begins . . . Drop the **e** from . . . with a vowel letter

_____

_____

2. **cvc** and the next . . . Double the final **c** . . . morphograph begins with **v** . . . in a short word when the word ends

_____

_____

Part B

Write each of these words in a box.

Write "free space" in one box.

reserve	carry	equally	consign	forceful	safely	latest	should

informer   package   happiness   boyish   rise   lengthen   were

CONSONANT−Y + ANYTHING, EXCEPT I

Part C

Add the morphographs together. Some of the words follow the rule about changing the **y** to **i** in a word.

1. study + ing = _____
2. study + ed = _____
3. dry + ly = _____
4. dry + ed = _____
5. dry + ing = _____
6. baby + ish = _____

7. dry + est = _____
8. nasty + ness = _____
9. play + er = _____
10. play + ing = _____
11. play + ful = _____
12. cry + er = _____

71

Lesson 45

Part D

Write **s** or **es** in the second column. Then add the morphographs together.

	s or es	plural word
1. buzz	+ _____	= _____
2. fan	+ _____	= _____
3. brother	+ _____	= _____
4. press	+ _____	= _____
5. stretch	+ _____	= _____
6. box	+ _____	= _____

Part E

Fill in the blanks to show the morphographs in each word.

1. _____ + _____ + _____ + _____ = unrefreshed
2. _____ + _____ = dropping
3. _____ + _____ + _____ = hopelessness
4. _____ + _____ = passage
5. _____ + _____ + _____ = unfitting
6. _____ + _____ = shining
7. _____ + _____ + _____ = unnerving
8. _____ + _____ = equally

PART	A	B	C	D	E	F	G	H	Worksheet Errors	Worksheet Points	Oral Points	Bonus Points	Total Points
											+	+	=

72

Part A

1. _____ + _____ = _____
2. _____ + _____ = _____
3. _____ + _____ = _____
4. _____ + _____ = _____
5. _____ + _____ = _____
6. _____ + _____ = _____

Part B

1. _____   4. _____
2. _____   5. _____
3. _____   6. _____

Part C

Make 10 real words from the morphographs in the box.

Some of the words will follow a rule, so be careful.

en	est	sad	mad	ness	wide	fine

1. _____   6. _____
2. _____   7. _____
3. _____   8. _____
4. _____   9. _____
5. _____   10. _____

Part D

Figure out the rules and write them. Remember to spell the words correctly.

1. word ends **cvc** and . . . Double the final **c** in . . . the next morphograph begins with **v** . . . a short word when

   the _____

   _____

2. word when the next . . . a vowel letter . . . morphograph begins with . . . Drop the **e** from a

   _____

   _____

73

Lesson 47

Part E

Fill in the blanks to show the morphographs in each word.

1. _____ + _____ = swimming
2. _____ + _____ + _____ = defacing
3. _____ + _____ = taken
4. _____ + _____ = sadden
5. _____ + _____ = choicest
6. _____ + _____ = forceful
7. _____ + _____ = racer
8. _____ + _____ = planning
9. _____ + _____ = signal
10. _____ + _____ + _____ = resigned
11. _____ + _____ = consign
12. _____ + _____ + _____ + _____ = unmistakable

Bonus Exercise

1. carry   carr ___   car ___ ___   ca ___ ___ ___   c ___ ___ ___ ___   ___ ___ ___ ___ ___
2. stretch   str ___ tch   st ___ ___ ___ ch   s ___ ___ ___ ___ ___ ___ h   ___ ___ ___ ___ ___ ___ h
3. change   cha ___ ___ e   ch ___ ___ ___ e   c ___ ___ ___ ___ ___   ___ ___ ___ ___ ___ ___
4. worry   w ___ rry   w ___ ___ ry   ___ ___ ___ ___ y   ___ ___ ___ ___ ___
5. civil   civ ___ l   ci ___ ___ l   c ___ ___ ___ l   ___ ___ ___ ___ l   ___ ___ ___ ___ ___

PART	A	B	C	D	E	F	G	H	Worksheet Errors	Worksheet Points	Oral Points	Bonus Points	Total Points
											+	+	=

74

Part A

1. _____   4. _____

2. _____   5. _____

3. _____   6. _____

Part B

Make 11 real words from the morphographs in the box.

Some of the words will follow a rule, so be careful.

| er   use   grade   ing   stop   able   trap |

1. _____   7. _____

2. _____   8. _____

3. _____   9. _____

4. _____   10. _____

5. _____   11. _____

6. _____

Part C

Add the morphographs together. Some of the words follow the rule about changing **y** to **i** in a word.

1. boy + ish   = _____

2. sturdy + ness = _____

3. worry + ed   = _____

4. pity + ful   = _____

5. baby + ish   = _____

6. farm + ing   = _____

7. carry + er   = _____

8. cry + ing   = _____

9. try + al   = _____

10. deny + al   = _____

11. stay + ed   = _____

12. fly + er   = _____

Lesson 48

Part D

These words are in the puzzle.

Circle 7 or more of the words.

civil	verb	carry	might
deny	robber	gone	dine
match	mad	does	easy

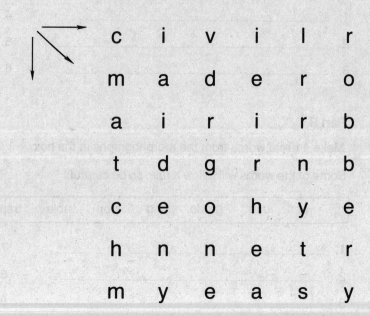

```
c  i  v  i  l  r
m  a  d  e  r  o
a  i  r  i  r  b
t  d  g  r  n  b
c  e  o  h  y  e
h  n  n  e  t  r
m  y  e  a  s  y
```

Part E

Fill in the blanks to show the morphographs in each word.

1. _____ + _____ = buzzes

2. _____ + _____ = barring

3. _____ + _____ = lonely

4. _____ + _____ = writing

5. _____ + _____ = signal

6. _____ + _____ = snapped

7. _____ + _____ + _____ = reserving

PART	A	B	C	D	E	F	G	H	Worksheet Errors	Worksheet Points	Oral Points	Bonus Points	Total Points
											+	+	=

Lesson 49

Part A

1. _____   4. _____

2. _____   5. _____

3. _____

Part B

1. could not = _____   5. he will   = _____

2. should not = _____   6. would not = _____

3. she is   = _____   7. I have   = _____

4. is not   = _____   8. you will = _____

Part C

1. _____

   _____

2. _____

   _____

Part D

1. _____ + _____ = _____

2. _____ + _____ = _____

3. _____ + _____ = _____

4. _____ + _____ = _____

5. _____ + _____ = _____

6. _____ + _____ = _____

7. _____ + _____ = _____

8. _____ + _____ = _____

Lesson 49

Part E

Make 11 real words from the morphographs in the box.

ing	shop	ful	hate	run	ed	er	hope

1. _____   7. _____

2. _____   8. _____

3. _____   9. _____

4. _____   10. _____

5. _____   11. _____

6. _____

Part F

Circle the misspelled word in each group. Then write it correctly in the blank.

1. other   2. story   3. whether   4. author

   cary   mispell   strength   mother

   wrong   sturdy   serve   buz

   could   fancy   strech   civil

   _____   _____   _____   _____

PART	A	B	C	D	E	F	G	H	Worksheet Errors	Worksheet Points	Oral Points	Bonus Points	Total Points
											+	+	=

Part A

1. _____
2. _____
3. _____

4. _____
5. _____
6. _____

Part B

Write contractions for the words in the first column.

contraction

1. were not = _____
2. does not = _____
3. are not = _____
4. she will = _____

contraction

5. you have = _____
6. did not = _____
7. can not = _____
8. they are = _____

Part C

Make 10 real words from the morphographs in the box.

Some of the words follow the rule about changing **y** to **i** in a word.

ful	ing	play	fancy	ed	er	pity

1. _____
2. _____
3. _____
4. _____
5. _____

6. _____
7. _____
8. _____
9. _____
10. _____

Part D

Figure out the rule and write it. Remember to spell the words correctly.

1. and the next morphograph begins with anything, ... when the word ends with a consonant-and-**y** ... except **i** ... Change the **y** to **i** in a word.

_____

_____

PART	A	B	C	D	E	F	G	H	Worksheet Errors	Worksheet Points	Oral Points	Bonus Points	Total Points
											+	+	=

Lesson 51

Part A

1. _____
2. _____
3. _____

4. _____
5. _____

Part B

1. _____
   _____
2. _____
   _____

Part C

Make 11 real words from the morphographs in the box.

est	nasty	er	ly	busy	dry	sturdy

1. _____
2. _____
3. _____
4. _____
5. _____
6. _____

7. _____
8. _____
9. _____
10. _____
11. _____

Part D

Write the word for each meaning. The words will contain these morphographs.

al - related to   **ful** - full of   **est** -the most

pre - before   **ish** - like   **en** - to make

	word	**meaning**
1.	_____	like a baby
2.	_____	the most late
3.	_____	related to signs
4.	_____	wrap before
5.	_____	make light
6.	_____	full of care

Part E

Write contractions for the words in the first column.

		contraction			**contraction**
1. let us	=	_____	5. we have	=	_____
2. have not	=	_____	6. what is	=	_____
3. was not	=	_____	7. he is	=	_____
4. they will	=	_____	8. would not	=	_____

Part F

Add these morphographs together.

1. swim + er	=	_____	5. mad + ly	=	_____
2. fine + est	=	_____	6. rage + ing	=	_____
3. wide + est	=	_____	7. trap + er	=	_____
4. con + sign	=	_____	8. un + civil + ly	=	_____

PART	A	B	C	D	E	F	G	H	Worksheet Errors	Worksheet Points	Oral Points	Bonus Points	Total Points
											+	+	=

Lesson 52

Part A

Complete each sentence correctly with one of these words:

write   right

1. My grandmother likes it when I _____ long letters.
2. Janis is the _____ person for the job.
3. My answers on the test were all _____.
4. When Martin was four years old, he could _____ his name.

Part B

Write the contractions for the words in the first column.

	contraction				contraction
1. has not =	_____		5. I will	=	_____
2. you are =	_____		6. they are =		_____
3. we will =	_____		7. were not =		_____
4. are not =	_____		8. it is	=	_____

Part C

Make 10 real words from the morphographs in the box.

deny	stay	ing	ed	able	dry	vary

1. _____   6. _____
2. _____   7. _____
3. _____   8. _____
4. _____   9. _____
5. _____   10. _____

Part D

Circle the misspelled word in each group. Then write it correctly in the blank.

1. worry	2. catch	3. hurring	4. claim
might	friend	fitness	queit
brother	wandor	whether	choice
civel	change	woman	equal

_____   _____   _____   _____

Part E

Fill in the blanks to show the morphographs in each word

1. _____ + _____ + _____ + _____ = unrefined
2. _____ + _____ + _____ = packaging
3. _____ + _____ + _____ = rightfully
4. _____ + _____ = inhuman
5. _____ + _____ + _____ = strengthening
6. _____ + _____ = lonely
7. _____ + _____ + _____ = helpfulness
8. _____ + _____ + _____ = unequally
9. _____ + _____ + _____ = resigned
10. _____ + _____ + _____ + _____ = unrelated

PART	A	B	C	D	E	F	G	H	Worksheet Errors	Worksheet Points	Oral Points	Bonus Points	Total Points
											+	+	=

83

Lesson 53

Part A

1. _____   4. _____
2. _____   5. _____
3. _____   6. _____

Part B

1. _____   7. _____
2. _____   8. _____
3. _____   9. _____
4. _____   10. _____
5. _____   11. _____
6. _____   12. _____

Part C

Write the contractions for the words in the first column.

           contraction   **contraction**

1. should not = _____   4. what is = _____
2. she is   = _____   5. they will = _____
3. I have   = _____   6. we are = _____

Part D

Make 8 real words from the morphographs in the box.

sound	ness	ly	est	happy	nasty

1. _____   5. _____
2. _____   6. _____
3. _____   7. _____
4. _____   8. _____

84

Part E

Figure out the rules and write them. Remember to spell the words correctly.

1. in a short word when the ` . . . next morphograph begins with **v** . . . Double the final **c** . . . word ends **cvc** and the

_____

_____

2. a consonant-and-**y** and the . . . a word when the word ends with . . . next morphograph begins with anything, except **i** . . . Change the **y** to **i** in

_____

_____

PART	A	B	C	D	E	F	G	H	Worksheet Errors	Worksheet Points	Oral Points	Bonus Points	Total Points
											+	+	=

Lesson 54

Part A

1. _____ + _____ = _____
2. _____ + _____ = _____
3. _____ + _____ = _____
4. _____ + _____ = _____
5. _____ + _____ = _____
6. _____ + _____ = _____
7. _____ + _____ = _____
8. _____ + _____ = _____

Part B

1. _____   5. _____
2. _____   6. _____
3. _____   7. _____
4. _____   8. _____

Part C

1. _____
   _____

2. _____
   _____

Part D

Make 11 real words from the morphographs in the box.

friend	ly	happy	ness	lone	sturdy	est

1. _____   7. _____
2. _____   8. _____
3. _____   9. _____
4. _____   10. _____
5. _____   11. _____
6. _____

Part E

Write the contractions for the words in the first column.

	contraction		**contraction**
1. can not	= _____	5. are not	= _____
2. does not	= _____	6. what is	= _____
3. they will	= _____	7. it is	= _____
4. you have	= _____	8. let us	= _____

Part F

1. _____ + _____ = sadder

2. _____ + _____ = strengthen

3. _____ + _____ + _____ = informal

4. _____ + _____ = useful

5. _____ + _____ = using

6. _____ + _____ + _____ = reserving

7. _____ + _____ + _____ = defacing

8. _____ + _____ = planning

PART	A	B	C	D	E	F	G	H	Worksheet Errors	Worksheet Points	Oral Points	Bonus Points	Total Points
											+	+	=

Lesson 56

Part A

1. _____ + _____ = _____
2. _____ + _____ = _____
3. _____ + _____ = _____
4. _____ + _____ = _____
5. _____ + _____ = _____
6. _____ + _____ = _____
7. _____ + _____ = _____
8. _____ + _____ = _____

Part B

Part C

Add these morphographs together. Some of the words follow the rule about dropping an **e**. Some of the words follow the rule about doubling.

1. re + move + al = _____
2. in + come = _____
3. rise + ing = _____
4. safe + ly = _____
5. hot + est = _____
6. mad + ness = _____
7. un+de+serve+ing = _____
8. use + age = _____
9. verb + al + ly = _____
10. re + cent +ly = _____
11. swim + er = _____
12. real + ly = _____

Part D

These words are in the puzzle.
Circle 7 or more of the words.

brotherly   report

spotted   race   neat

traps   stay   loud   vary

whether   length   cared

```
b  r  c  l  s  n  t  l  w
r  r  u  a  o  u  u  e  h
s  e  o  n  r  u  o  n  e
s  p  o  t  t  e  d  g  t
s  o  a  y  h  n  d  t  h
s  r  a  c  e  e  e  h  e
l  t  r  a  p  s  r  a  r
v  t  a  t  o  r  t  l  t
v  a  r  y  y  r  h  h  y
```

Part E

Complete each sentence correctly with one of these words:

vary   write   right   whole

1. Tony's new shoes are exactly the _____ size.

2. Instead of eating the same thing all the time, you should _____ your diet.

3. My uncle was so hungry last Sunday that he ate a _____ chicken.

4. Joggers don't usually run at the same speed all the time. They usually _____ their pace.

5. The blanks on your worksheet are where you _____ spelling words.

6. Last Friday we worked hard the _____ day.

PART	A	B	C	D	E	F	G	H	Worksheet Errors	Worksheet Points	Oral Points	Bonus Points	Total Points
											+	+	=

89

Lesson 57

Part A

	s or es	plural word			s or es	plural word
1. worry +	_____	= _____	6. boy +	_____	= _____
2. story +	_____	= _____	7. play +	_____	= _____
3. try +	_____	= _____	8. study +	_____	= _____
4. joy +	_____	= _____	9. stay +	_____	= _____
5. copy +	_____	= _____	10. carry +	_____	= _____

Part B

1. _____ 4. _____

2. _____ 5. _____

3. _____

Part C

1. _____ 5. _____

2. _____ 6. _____

3. _____ 7. _____

4. _____

Part D

Circle the misspelled word in each group. Then write it correctly in the blank.

1. proud	2. wander	3. auther
strength	equil	hurry
mispell	civil	sturdy
wrong	friendly	whether
_____	_____	_____

4. pleaze	5. file	6. sirve
straight	should	farmer
whose	happiness	swimmer
about	realy	fancy
_____	_____	_____

Part E

Fill in the blanks to show the morphographs in each word.

1. _____ + _____ = conform

2. _____ + _____ = consign

3. _____ + _____ = reserve

4. _____ + _____ + _____ = conserving

5. _____ + _____ = inform

6. _____ + _____ = equally

7. _____ + _____ = runner

Bonus Exercise

1. **straight**   str ___ ___ght   str ___ ___ ___ ___t   s ___ ___ ___ ___ ___t   ___ ___ ___ ___ ___ ___ ___ ___

2. **strength**   str ___ ___gth   s ___ ___ ___ ___ ___h   ___ ___ ___ ___ ___ ___ ___ ___

3. **stretch**   str ___tch   str ___ ___ch   str ___ ___ ___ ___   ___ ___ ___ ___ ___ ___ ___

4. **whether**   whe ___ ___er   wh ___ ___ ___ ___r   w ___ ___ ___ ___ ___ ___   ___ ___ ___ ___ ___ ___ ___

PART	A	B	C	D	E	F	G	H	Worksheet Errors	Worksheet Points	Oral Points	Bonus Points	Total Points
											+	+	=

91

Lesson 58

Part A

	s or es	plural word			s or es	plural word
1. stay	+ _____	= _____	5. worry	+ _____	= _____
2. copy	+ _____	= _____	6. fly	+ _____	= _____
3. toy	+ _____	= _____	7. boy	+ _____	= _____
4. spray	+ _____	= _____	8. carry	+ _____	= _____

Part B

1. _____ 3. _____

2. _____ 4. _____

Part C

Fill in the blanks to show the morphographs in each word.

1. _____ + _____ = proclaim

2. _____ + _____ = express

3. _____ + _____ = profuse

4. _____ + _____ = profit

5. _____ + _____ = consign

6. _____ + _____ = conserve

7. _____ + _____ = relate

Part D

Figure out the rules and write them. Remember to spell the words correctly.

1. next morphograph begins with . . .Drop the **e** . . .a vowel letter . . .from a word when the

_____

_____

2. next morphograph begins with **v** . . . short word when the . . . Double the final **c** in a . . . word ends **cvc** and the

_____

_____

Part E

Add these morphographs together. Some of the words follow spelling rules.

1. vary + ed = _____

2. rise + ing = _____

3. trap + er = _____

4. study + ing = _____

5. straight + en = _____

6. strength + en = _____

7. nasty + ly = _____

8. lone + ly = _____

9. un + equal + ly = _____

10. human + ness = _____

11. dine + ing = _____

12. force + ful = _____

PART	A	B	C	D	E	F	G	H	Worksheet Errors	Worksheet Points	Oral Points	Bonus Points	Total Points
											+	+	=

Lesson 59

Part A

		s or es		plural word				s or es		plural word
1.	boy	+ _____	=	_____		5.	baby	+ _____	=	_____
2.	story	+ _____	=	_____		6.	fly	+ _____	=	_____
3.	try	+ _____	=	_____		7.	berry	+ _____	=	_____
4.	worry	+ _____	=	_____		8.	carry	+ _____	=	_____

Part B

1. _____   3. _____

2. _____   4. _____

Part C

1. _____   4. _____

2. _____   5. _____

3. _____

Part D

Write the contractions for the words in the first column.

		contraction			contraction
1. were not	=	_____	5. let us	=	_____
2. have not	=	_____	6. are not	=	_____
3. you will	=	_____	7. would not	=	_____
4. they had	=	_____	8. does not	=	_____

Part E

Complete each sentence correctly with one of these words:

write   vary   whole   very   right   hole

1. Parachute jumping is a _____ exciting sport.

2. Whenever you misspell a word, you should _____ that word correctly at least one time.

3. A woodpecker made a small _____ in the side of our barn.

4. I like to do a different set of exercises every day. My friends also _____ their exercises.

5. No one thought Sandy would finish her book, but she read the _____ story anyway.

6. The Marche Company hasn't hired a shipping clerk because they haven't found the _____ person for the job.

Part F

Fill in the blanks to show the morphographs in each word.

1. _____ + _____ = relate

2. _____ + _____ + _____ = actively

3. _____ + _____ + _____ = expressive

4. _____ + _____ + _____ = relative

5. _____ + _____ + _____ = inactive

6. _____ + _____ + _____ = removal

7. _____ + _____ + _____ = remaining

8. _____ + _____ = signal

PART	A	B	C	D	E	F	G	H	Worksheet Errors	Worksheet Points	Oral Points	Bonus Points	Total Points
											+	+	=

Lesson 60

Part A

		s or es	plural word			s or es	plural word
1. study	+ _____	= _____		5. cry	+ _____	= _____
2. story	+ _____	= _____		6. joy	+ _____	= _____
3. play	+ _____	= _____		7. city	+ _____	= _____
4. glory	+ _____	= _____		8. fly	+ _____	= _____

Part B

1. _____
2. _____
3. _____
4. _____

5. _____
6. _____
7. _____
8. _____

Part C

1. _____
2. _____
3. _____

4. _____
5. _____

Part D

Make 11 real words from the morphographs in the box.

Some of the words follow the doubling rule.

Some of the words follow the **y** to **i** rule.

hot	ly	sturdy	er	mad	nasty	est

1. _____
2. _____
3. _____
4. _____
5. _____
6. _____

7. _____
8. _____
9. _____
10. _____
11. _____

PART	A	B	C	D	E	F	G	H	Worksheet Errors	Worksheet Points	Oral Points	Bonus Points	Total Points
											+	+	=

96

Part A

1. _____   4. _____

2. _____   5. _____

6. _____

Part B

	s or **es**	**plural word**

1. copy + _____ = _____   5. city + _____ = _____

2. spray + _____ = _____   6. worry + _____ = _____

3. fly + _____ = _____   7. study + _____ = _____

4. boy + _____ = _____   8. story + _____ = _____

Part C

1. _____

2. _____

3. _____

4. _____

Part D

Draw a line from each word to its meaning

very •   • all parts together

right •   • putting words on paper

vary •   • an empty space

whole •   • really

write •   • correct

hole •   • change

Part E

Fill in the blanks to show the morphographs in each word.

1. _____ + _____ = passive

2. _____ + _____ = proverb

3. _____ + _____ = exchange

4. _____ + _____ = relate

5. _____ + _____ + _____ = relative

6. _____ + _____ = reserve

PART	A	B	C	D	E	F	G	H	Worksheet Errors	Worksheet Points	Oral Points	Bonus Points	Total Points
											+	+	=

97

Lesson 62

Part A

1. _____   6. _____
2. _____   7. _____
3. _____   8. _____
4. _____   9. _____
5. _____   10. _____

Part B

1. _____

_____

2. _____

_____

Part C

Write the contractions for the words in the first column.

         contraction   **contraction**

1. what is = _____   4. he will = _____

2. would not = _____   5. are not = _____

3. can not = _____   6. it is = _____

Part D

Write **s** or **es** in the second column. Then add the morphographs together.

       s or **es**   **s** or **es**

1. tax   + _____ = _____   5. copy   + _____ = _____

2. study + _____ = _____   6. thought + _____ = _____

3. play + _____ = _____   7. worry + _____ = _____

4. brush + _____ = _____   8. spray + _____ = _____

Part E

Figure out the rules and write them. Remember to spell the words correctly.

1. **c** in a short word when . . .morphograph begins with **v** . . .the word ends . . .double the final . . .**cvc** and the next

_____

_____

2. a word when the word ends with . . .next morphograph begins with anything, except **i** . . .a consonant-and-**y** and the . . .change the **y** to **i** in

_____

_____

Part F

Draw a line from each word to its meaning.

write •   • all parts together

hole •   • really

whole •   • putting words on paper

vary •   • correct

right •   • change

very •   • an empty space

PART	A	B	C	D	E	F	G	H	Worksheet Errors	Worksheet Points	Oral Points	Bonus Points	Total Points
											+	+	=

99

Lesson 63

Part A

1. _____   5. _____
2. _____   6. _____
3. _____   7. _____
4. _____   8. _____

Part B

Fill in the blanks to show the morphographs in each word.

1. _____ + _____ + _____ = repression
2. _____ + _____ + _____ + _____ = uninformed
3. _____ + _____ + _____ = inactive
4. _____ + _____ + _____ = thoughtlessly
5. _____ + _____ = foxes
6. _____ + _____ = berries
7. _____ + _____ + _____ = joyfully
8. _____ + _____ + _____ = replacing

Part C

Look at the lst three letters of each word.
Make a **v** or a **c** above each of the last three letters.
Circle each short word that ends **cvc**.

1. under   3. grow   5. fur   7. show   9. whether

2. boy   4. fit   6. snap   8. bar   10. stay

Part D

Add these morphographs together. Remember to use your spelling rules.

1. please + ing = _____
2. worry + es = _____
3. neat + ness = _____
4. study + ing = _____
5. sad + ness = _____

6. re + late + ive = _____
7. story + es = _____
8. fit + ing = _____
9. pity + ful = _____
10. wrap + er = _____

Part E

Draw a line from each word to its meaning.

vary •

whole •

right •

write •

very •

feat •

hole •

• all parts together

• doing something great

• change

• correct

• really

• an empty space

• putting words on paper

PART	A	B	C	D	E	F	G	H	Worksheet Errors	Worksheet Points	Oral Points	Bonus Points	Total Points
											+	+	=

Lesson 64

Part A

1. _____   6. _____
2. _____   7. _____
3. _____   8. _____
4. _____   9. _____
5. _____   10. _____

Part B

1. _____ + _____ = _____
2. _____ + _____ = _____
3. _____ + _____ = _____
4. _____ + _____ = _____
5. _____ + _____ = _____
6. _____ + _____ = _____
7. _____ + _____ = _____
8. _____ + _____ = _____
9. _____ + _____ = _____
10. _____ + _____ = _____

Part C

Complete each sentence correctly with one of these words:

feat   write   whole   vary

1. The detective wasn't able to solve his case until he heard the _____ story.

2. Jan swam across the raging river, which was a brave _____ .

3. I used to always print my name, but now I _____ it.

4. The restaurants on Miller Street are popular because they _____ their menus daily.

5. A strongman at the circus performed a different _____ of strength during every intermission.

Part D

Make 11 real words from the morphographs in the box.

less	thought	ness	hope	ly	ful

1. _____   7. _____

2. _____   8. _____

3. _____   9. _____

4. _____   10. _____

5. _____   11. _____

6. _____

Part E

Add these morphographs together. Remember to use your spelling rules.

1. un + happy + ly = _____

2. care + les + ly = _____

3. snap + er = _____

4. deny + al = _____

5. lone + ly = _____

6. ex + claim + ed = _____

7. stop + age = _____

8. re + move + al = _____

PART	A	B	C	D	E	F	G	H	Worksheet Errors	Worksheet Points	Oral Points	Bonus Points	Total Points
											+	+	=

Lesson 65

Part A

1. _____ + _____ = _____
2. _____ + _____ = _____
3. _____ + _____ = _____
4. _____ + _____ = _____

Part B

1. _____
2. _____
3. _____
4. _____

Part C

1. _____
2. _____
3. _____
4. _____
5. _____
6. _____

Part D

Fill in the blanks to show the morphographs in each word.

1. _____ + _____ = passion
2. _____ + _____ = passive
3. _____ + _____ = action
4. _____ + _____ = active
5. _____ + _____ = proverb
6. _____ + _____ = export
7. _____ + _____ = profound
8. _____ + _____ = exact

Part E

Circle the misspelled word in each group. Then write it correctly in the blank.

1. fluid
   poison
   strate
   about

   _____

2. glory
   pleaze
   place
   civil

   _____

3. brother
   wrong
   carry
   hopeing

   _____

4. proud
   whose
   berry
   werry

   _____

5. queit
   stretch
   friend
   wander

   _____

6. choice
   equil
   strength
   studying

   _____

7. studyes
   author
   neatly
   depressed

   _____

8. swimmer
   serving
   pitiful
   maddness

   _____

PART	A	B	C	D	E	F	G	H	Worksheet Errors	Worksheet Points	Oral Points	Bonus Points	Total Points
											+	+	=

Lesson 66

Part A

1. _____ 3. _____

2. _____ 4. _____

Part B

1. _____ 4. _____

2. _____ 5. _____

3. _____

Part C

Write **s** or **es** in the second column. Then add the morphographs together.

           s or **es**   **s** or **es**

1. glory + _____ = _____ 5. buzz + _____ = _____

2. stay + _____ = _____ 6. joy + _____ = _____

3. press + _____ = _____ 7. deny + _____ = _____

4. fury + _____ = _____ 8. pity + _____ = _____

Part D

Fill in the blanks to show the morphographs in each word.

1. _____ + _____ = repress

2. _____ + _____ + _____ = repression

3. _____ + _____ + _____ = repressive

4. _____ + _____ + _____ = expression

5. _____ + _____ + _____ = expressive

6. _____ + _____ = feature

Part E

Add these morphographs together. Remember to use your spelling rules.

1. strength + en + ing = _____ 6. trap + er = _____

2. poison + ed = _____ 7. happy + ness = _____

3. hurry + ed = _____ 8. straight + en + ing = _____

4. carry + ing = _____ 9. proud + ly = _____

5. pro + claim + ed = _____ 10. late + ly = _____

PART	A	B	C	D	E	F	G	H	Worksheet Errors	Worksheet Points	Oral Points	Bonus Points	Total Points
											+	+	=

106

Part A

1. _____ + _____ = _____
2. _____ + _____ = _____
3. _____ + _____ = _____
4. _____ + _____ = _____

Part B

1. _____
2. _____
3. _____
4. _____
5. _____
6. _____

Part C

1. _____
2. _____
3. _____
4. _____
5. _____
6. _____
7. _____
8. _____

Part D

Draw a line from each word to its meaning.

write •   • really

vary •   • the things you walk on

feat •   • correct

whole •   • putting words on paper

very •   • all parts together

right •   • an empty space

feet •   • change

hole •   • doing something great

Lesson 67

Part E

Fill in the blanks to show the morphographs in each word.

1. _____ + _____ = preside

2. _____ + _____ = action

3. _____ + _____ = pressure

4. _____ + _____ = passive

5. _____ + _____ + _____ = relative

6. _____ + _____ = active

7. _____ + _____ = poisonous

8. _____ + _____ = feature

9. _____ + _____ + _____ = gloriously

10. _____ + _____ + _____ = formally

PART	A	B	C	D	E	F	G	H	Worksheet Errors	Worksheet Points	Oral Points	Bonus Points	Total Points
											+	+	=

Part A

1. _____
2. _____
3. _____
4. _____
5. _____

6. _____
7. _____
8. _____
9. _____
10. _____

Part B

Write each of these words in a box. Write "free space" in one box.

equally	defile	motherly	ruinous	studies
blow	depression	texture	preserve	feature
straight	various	they're	passion	babies

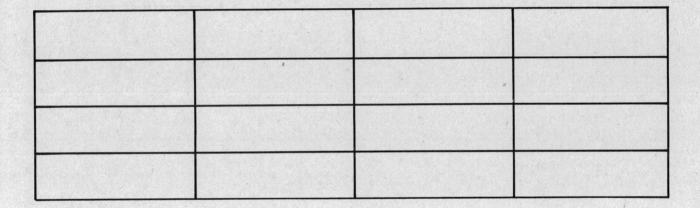

Part C

Write **s** or **es** in the second column. Then add the morphographs together.

1. cry   + _____ = _____
2. box   + _____ = _____
3. vary   + _____ = _____
4. stay   + _____ = _____

5. story   + _____ = _____
6. friend   + _____ = _____
7. glory   + _____ = _____
8. play   + _____ = _____

Lesson 68

Part D

Circle the misspelled word in each group. Then write it correctly in the blank.

1. strength
   poisen
   fluid
   thought
   _____

2. worryes
   wrong
   studies
   brother
   _____

3. straight
   count
   realy
   change
   _____

4. friendly
   quietly
   author
   sturdyly
   _____

5. woman
   fansy
   copies
   swimmer
   _____

6. preserving
   joyously
   equall
   civilly
   _____

PART	A	B	C	D	E	F	G	H	Worksheet Errors	Worksheet Points	Oral Points	Bonus Points	Total Points
											+	+	=

Part A

1. _____
2. _____
3. _____

4. _____
5. _____

Part B

1. _____
   _____
2. _____
   _____

Part C

1. _____
2. _____
3. _____
4. _____

5. _____
6. _____
7. _____
8. _____

Part D

Make 11 real words from the morphographs in the box.

est	happy	wide	ly	fine	ness	mad

1. _____
2. _____
3. _____
4. _____
5. _____
6. _____

7. _____
8. _____
9. _____
10. _____
11. _____

Lesson 69

Part E

Fill in the blanks to show the morphographs in each word.

1. _____ + _____ + _____ = protective
2. _____ + _____ + _____ = injection
3. _____ + _____ + _____ = progressed
4. _____ + _____ + _____ = reception
5. _____ + _____ = texture
6. _____ + _____ = feature
7. _____ + _____ = passion
8. _____ + _____ = studying
9. _____ + _____ = studious
10. _____ + _____ = signal

Part F

Circle the words in the lines.

1. (prove)   provprovepruveproreproveprproveeprov
2. (thought) thoughtthouhgtthoughttthoughtthoughttthought
3. (straight) straihgtstraightsstraightstraightstraigth
4. (whether) whetherwetherwhetherwhwhetherwhethrwhether

PART	A	B	C	D	E	F	G	H	Worksheet Errors	Worksheet Points	Oral Points	Bonus Points	Total Points
											+	+	=

Part A

1. _____
2. _____
3. _____

4. _____
5. _____

Part B

1. _____
2. _____
3. _____
4. _____

5. _____
6. _____
7. _____
8. _____

Part C

Add these morphographs together. Remember to use your spelling rules.

1. poison + ous   = _____

2. re + gain + ed   = _____

3. pause + ing   = _____

4. un + prove + en   = _____

5. fur + y   = _____

6. re + fuse + al   = _____

7. in + act + ion   = _____

8. ex + press + ive   = _____

9. fuse + ion   = _____

10. mis + place + ed   = _____

11. pro + claim + ed   = _____

12. spray + ed   = _____

13. please + ure   = _____

14. friend + ly + ness   = _____

15. carry + ed   = _____

Lesson 70

Part D

Circle the misspelled word in each group. Then write it correctly in the blank.

1. giving	2. fluids	3. brain	4. feature
detect	varies	reseptive	loudness
lenght	concept	pressure	dineing
hurried	furyous	washes	except

_____ _____ _____ _____

Part E

1. _____ + _____ = extent
2. _____ + _____ = content
3. _____ + _____ + _____ = intention
4. _____ + _____ = reside
5. _____ + _____ = inside
6. _____ + _____ = proven

PART	A	B	C	D	E	F	G	H	Worksheet Errors	Worksheet Points	Oral Points	Bonus Points	Total Points
											+	+	=

Part A

1. _____
2. _____
3. _____
4. _____
5. _____
6. _____

Part B

1. _____
2. _____
3. _____
4. _____
5. _____
6. _____
7. _____
8. _____

Part C

1. _____ = reporting
2. _____ = photograph
3. _____ = intent
4. _____ = content
5. _____ = cloudy
6. _____ = poisonous
7. _____ = strengthening
8. _____ = physics

Part D

These words are in the puzzle.
Circle 7 or more of the words.

poison   found   photo

pound   concept   flat

lone   pity   whose

store   fact   proven

```
p  p  w  h  o  s  e  f
p  o  i  s  o  n  s  p
c  o  n  c  e  p  t  r
f  o  u  n  d  h  o  o
a  l  o  n  e  o  r  v
c  p  a  r  d  t  e  e
t  p  i  t  y  o  e  n
```

Lesson 71

Part E

Add these morphographs together. Remember to use your spelling rules.

1. fury + ous   = _____

2. pain + less + ly = _____

3. pro + gress + ive = _____

4. sore + ness   = _____

5. text + ure + ed   = _____

6. story + es   = _____

7. please + ure   = _____

8. hot + est   = _____

9. force + ful   = _____

10. ex + act + ly   = _____

11. pro + found + ly = _____

12. feat + ure   = _____

PART	A	B	C	D	E	F	G	H	Worksheet Errors	Worksheet Points	Oral Points	Bonus Points	Total Points
											+	+	=

Part A

1. _____
2. _____
3. _____
4. _____
5. _____
6. _____

Part B

1. _____
2. _____
3. _____
4. _____
5. _____
6. _____
7. _____
8. _____

Part C

1. _____
2. _____
3. _____
4. _____
5. _____
6. _____
7. _____
8. _____

Part D

Complete each sentence correctly with one of these words:

hole   right   varied   features   write

1. Murphy's Cafe _____ fried chicken every Friday.

2. Caron's experiment failed, but she had the _____ idea.

3. The marking of Holly's puppies _____ greatly.

4. Our boat won't float because it has a large _____ in the bottom.

5. Since our new car doesn't run well, we are going to _____ a letter to the company that made it.

Lesson 72

Part E

Fill in the blanks to show the morphographs in each word.
Write the morphographs with plus signs in between them.

1. _____ = physical

2. _____ = physics

3. _____ = famous

4. _____ = photography

5. _____ = consent

6. _____ = regain

7. _____ = resent

8. _____ = spinner

9. _____ = retained

10. _____ = concept

PART	A	B	C	D	E	F	G	H	Worksheet Errors	Worksheet Points	Oral Points	Bonus Points	Total Points
											+	+	=

Part A

Part B

1. _____ + _____ = _____
2. _____ + _____ = _____
3. _____ + _____ = _____
4. _____ + _____ = _____

Part C

Circle each short word that ends **cvc**.

Remember: **y** and **w** are vowels at the end of a morphograph
x acts like two consonant letters
short words have 3 or 4 letters

1. gain

2. know

3. spin

4. woman

5. man

6. show

7. boy

8. box

9. swim

10. trap

11. brother

12. win

Lesson 74

Part D

Add these morphographs together. Remember your spelling rules.

1. happy + ness = _____

2. ease + y = _____

3. thought + ful = _____

4. spin + ing = _____

5. sure + ly = _____

6. dis + prove + en = _____

7. feat + ure = _____

8. trap + er = _____

Part E

Fill in the blanks to show the morphographs in each word.
Write the morphographs with plus signs in between them.

1. _____ = resign

2. _____ = signal

3. _____ = relate

4. _____ = busily

5. _____ = receptive

6. _____ = relative

7. _____ = pleasing

8. _____ = pleasure

PART	A	B	C	D	E	F	G	H	Worksheet Errors	Worksheet Points	Oral Points	Bonus Points	Total Points
											+	+	=

Part A

1. _____
2. _____
3. _____
4. _____
5. _____
6. _____

7. _____
8. _____
9. _____
10. _____
11. _____
12. _____

Part B

1. _____
2. _____

3. _____
4. _____

Part C

Make 9 real words from the morphographs in the box.

| ly | glory | nerve | ous | joy | study | vary |

1. _____
2. _____
3. _____
4. _____
5. _____
6. _____
7. _____
8. _____
9. _____

Lesson 75

Part D

Draw a line from each word to its meaning.

cent •   • doing something great

feat •   • correct

vary •   • putting words on paper

whole •   • one hundred

write •   • change

very •   • really

right •   • all parts together

Part E

Circle the misspelled word in each group. Then write it correctly on the line.

1. proove	2. civil	3. fone	4. could'nt
phone	thoughtful	brain	trapper
shore	starrless	shouldn't	studies
straight	graph	wrong	lately

_____   _____   _____   _____

PART	A	B	C	D	E	F	G	H	Worksheet Errors	Worksheet Points	Oral Points	Bonus Points	Total Points
											+	+	=

Part A

1. _____ 3. _____

2. _____ 4. _____

Part B

1. _____

_____

2. _____

_____

Part C

The woman put the boxs of poisen   _____

in a safe plase.   _____

We spraied the moter with cleaning   _____

fluid.   _____

                                          _____

Part D

Write **s** or **es** in the second column. Then add the morphographs together.

        s or **es**   **s** or **es**

1. spray + _____ = _____   5. stretch + _____ = _____

2. catch + _____ = _____   6. hurry + _____ = _____

3. vary   + _____ = _____   7. stay   + _____ = _____

4. dry   + _____ = _____   8. fry   + _____ = _____

Part E

Figure out the rule and write it. Remember to spell the words correctly.

a word when the word ends with...next morphograph begins with anything except **i**...a consonant-and-**y** and the...change the **y** to **i** in

_____

_____

PART	A	B	C	D	E	F	G	H	Worksheet Errors	Worksheet Points	Oral Points	Bonus Points	Total Points
											+	+	=

Lesson 77

Part A

1. _____
2. _____
3. _____
4. _____
5. _____

Part B

1. _____
2. _____
3. _____
4. _____
5. _____
6. _____
7. _____
8. _____

Part C

1. _____
2. _____
3. _____
4. _____

Part D

Circle the misspelled word in each group. Then write it correctly on the line.

1. feature	2. hopeful	3. portabel	4. lose
any	blissfull	rise	fone
poisonus	stopper	herbal	passage
fly	friend	traps	shouldn't

_____ _____ _____ _____

5. rental	6. reported	7. lightly	8. hopefulnes
work	finest	hotest	about
eqwip	retract	catcher	thoughtful
passive	disstract	driest	furious

_____ _____ _____ _____

Part E

Draw a line from each word to its meaning.

cent	●		●	an empty space
vary	●		●	putting words on paper
write	●		●	one hundred
whole	●		●	really
feat	●		●	change
right	●		●	all parts together
very	●		●	correct
hole	●		●	doing something great

PART	A	B	C	D	E	F	G	H	Worksheet Errors	Worksheet Points	Oral Points	Bonus Points	Total Points
											+	+	=

Lesson 78

Part A

1. _____ 4. _____
2. _____ 5. _____
3. _____

Part B

1. _____ 3. _____
2. _____ 4. _____

Part C

1. _____ 5. _____
2. _____ 6. _____
3. _____ 7. _____
4. _____ 8. _____

Part D

Write the contractions for the words in the first column.

<table>
<tr><td></td><td>contraction</td><td></td><td>contraction</td></tr>
<tr><td>1. were not =</td><td>_____</td><td>5. are not =</td><td>_____</td></tr>
<tr><td>2. they will =</td><td>_____</td><td>6. did not =</td><td>_____</td></tr>
<tr><td>3. does not =</td><td>_____</td><td>7. they are =</td><td>_____</td></tr>
<tr><td>4. I have =</td><td>_____</td><td>8. we have =</td><td>_____</td></tr>
</table>

Part E

Add these morphographs together. Remember to use your spelling rules.

1. state + ing   = _____
2. vise + ion   = _____
3. physic + al   = _____
4. re + sent + ed   = _____
5. re + quest + ing   = _____
6. duty + es   = _____

7. spin + er   = _____
8. heavy + est   = _____
9. mis + shape + en   = _____
10. fame + ous   = _____
11. re + late + ive   = _____

PART	A	B	C	D	E	F	G	H	Worksheet Errors	Worksheet Points	Oral Points	Bonus Points	Total Points
											+	+	=

126

Part A

1. _____

_____

2. _____

Part B

1. _____ 4. _____

2. _____ 5. _____

3. _____

Part C

Fill in the blanks to show the morphographs in each word.

1. _____ = question

2. _____ = breathless

3. _____ = resigned

4. _____ = revise

5. _____ = vision

6. _____ = photograph

7. _____ = cloudy

8. _____ = shiny

9. _____ = trying

10. _____ = trial

Part D

Complete each sentence correctly with one of these words:

sent   cent   tail   feet   various

1. We saw an old jet plane with an orange ball on its _____ .

2. The new candy bars are twenty-five per _____ smaller than the old ones.

3. No one received our Christmas presents on time last year because we _____ them too late.

4. After a long hike in the mountains, my _____ are usually sore for a week.

5. We tried all the _____ rides at the fair.

6. Our dog caught its _____ in the back door.

PART	A	B	C	D	E	F	G	H	Worksheet Errors	Worksheet Points	Oral Points	Bonus Points	Total Points
											+	+	=

127

Lesson 80

Part A

1. _____ 4. _____

2. _____ 5. _____

3. _____ 6. _____

Part B

These words are in the puzzle.
Circle 7 or more of the words.

fact   know   wrap

diet   chief   heroic

win   fly   detect

tin   niece   reject

```
k  t  n  k  n  o  w
f  r  i  d  c  w  r
d  a  e  n  h  i  a
k  i  c  j  i  n  p
n  d  e  t  e  c  t
f  l  y  t  f  c  y
h  e  r  o  i  c  t
```

Part C

Draw a line from each word to its meaning.

sent •   • change

plain •   • all parts together

cent •   • doing something great

tail •   • one hundred

vary •   • moved somewhere

right •   • ordinary

feat •   • the end

whole •   • correct

Part D

Circle the misspelled word in each group. Then write it correctly on the line.

1. racing
   friendlyness
   helpful
   buzzy
   _____

2. boxs
   fits
   staying
   naming
   _____

3. hoping
   raging
   easey
   serve
   _____

4. poisonous
   civilly
   changer
   bigest
   _____

5. caged
   stepping
   berrys
   fittest
   _____

6. taken
   feeture
   grandest
   notable
   _____

7. sprayyer
   various
   remove
   couldn't
   _____

8. paused
   growing
   replace
   wonderring
   _____

PART	A	B	C	D	E	F	G	H	Worksheet Errors	Worksheet Points	Oral Points	Bonus Points	Total Points
											+	+	=

Lesson 81

Part A

1. _____
2. _____
3. _____
4. _____
5. _____
6. _____

Part B

1. _____
2. _____
3. _____
4. _____
5. _____
6. _____

Part C

1. _____
_____
2. _____
_____

Part D

Fill in the blanks to show the morphographs in each word.

1. _____ = questionable
2. _____ = thirsty
3. _____ = explained
4. _____ = failure
5. _____ = request
6. _____ = rejection
7. _____ = stately
8. _____ = station
9. _____ = reducing
10. _____ = dispel
11. _____ = biggest
12. _____ = hopping

Part E

Look at the last three letters of each word. Circle each short word that ends **cvc**.

1. poison
2. ship
3. know
4. bet
5. plant
6. about
7. joy
8. civil
9. spin
10. hop

PART	A	B	C	D	E	F	G	H	Worksheet Errors	Worksheet Points	Oral Points	Bonus Points	Total Points
											+	+	=

130

Part A

I thougth my brothor woold
photograf our neice.

_____

_____

_____

The pain in Mark's hed was cured
with some kind of ingection.

_____

_____

_____

_____

_____

Part B

1. _____   5. _____

2. _____   6. _____

3. _____   7. _____

4. _____   8. _____

Part C

1. _____   4. _____

2. _____   5. _____

3. _____   6. _____

Part D

Complete each sentence correctly with one of these words:

right   various   sent   tail

1. I _____ away for a book, but it never came.

2. Martin's desk is always cluttered with _____ things.

3. Ellen must have said the _____ thing because she did get the job.

4. Lee made a _____ for her kite out of rags.

5. Jill got more answers _____ than Jack did.

Lesson 82

Part E

Figure out the rules and write them. Remember to spell the words correctly.

1. word when the word ends with a . . . with anything, except **i** . . . change the **y** to **i** in a . . . consonant-and-**y** and . . . the next morphograph begins

_____

_____

2. vowel letter . . .next morphograph begins with a . . .from a word when the . . .drop the **e**

_____

_____

PART	A	B	C	D	E	F	G	H	Worksheet Errors	Worksheet Points	Oral Points	Bonus Points	Total Points
											+	+	=

Part A

1. _____ 4. _____
2. _____ 5. _____
3. _____ 6. _____

Part B

1. _____ 4. _____
2. _____ 5. _____
3. _____ 6. _____

Part C

1. _____ 5. _____
2. _____ 6. _____
3. _____ 7. _____
4. _____ 8. _____

Part D

Draw a line from each word to its meaning.

tail •   • the things you walk on

tale •   • correct

sent •   • doing something great

cent •   • a story

feat •   • the end

feet •   • moved somewhere

whole •   • one hundred

right •   • all parts together

Lesson 84

Part E

Fill in the blanks to show the morphographs in each word.

1. _____ = recover

2. _____ = explain

3. _____ = preserved

4. _____ = hopping

5. _____ = hoping

6. _____ = business

7. _____ = cloudy

8. _____ = easy

9. _____ = relative

10. _____ = retraction

11. _____ = propel

12. _____ = retained

13. _____ = reducing

14. _____ = wrapper

15. _____ = famous

PART	A	B	C	D	E	F	G	H	Worksheet Errors	Worksheet Points	Oral Points	Bonus Points	Total Points
											+	+	=

Part A

1. _____ 2. _____ 3. _____

Part B

1. _____ 5. _____
2. _____ 6. _____
3. _____ 7. _____
4. _____ 8. _____

Part C

1. _____ 4. _____
2. _____ 5. _____
3. _____ 6. _____

Part D

Fill in the blanks to show the morphographs in each word.

1. _____ = extent
2. _____ = failure
3. _____ = business
4. _____ = content
5. _____ = contract
6. _____ = glorious
7. _____ = studious
8. _____ = extract

Lesson 85

Part E

Circle the mispelled word in each group. Then write it correctly in the blank.

1. hyuman
   carelessness
   hopeful
   rental
   _____

2. discoverer
   safeer
   whose
   you've
   _____

3. Il'l
   neatest
   income
   displease
   _____

4. active
   misplace
   rezerve
   deport
   _____

5. denying
   clannish
   fanciness
   nameable
   _____

6. straghtest
   profuse
   edition
   equally
   _____

7. pause
   resort
   pasive
   defeat
   _____

8. babied
   lonly
   throwing
   proving
   _____

PART	A	B	C	D	E	F	G	H	Worksheet Errors	Worksheet Points	Oral Points	Bonus Points	Total Points
											+	+	=

Part A

1. _____   4. _____

2. _____   5. _____

3. _____

Part B

1. _____   6. _____

2. _____   7. _____

3. _____   8. _____

4. _____   9. _____

5. _____   10. _____

Part C

Lesson 86

Part D

Write contractions for the words in the first column.

		contraction				contraction
1. are not	=	_____	5. she will	=	_____
2. we have	=	_____	6. were not	=	_____
3. does not	=	_____	7. they are	=	_____
4. could not	=	_____	8. they have	=	_____

Part E

Add these morphographs together. Remember to use your spelling rules.

1. chance + es   = _____

2. ship + er   = _____

3. thirst + y + ly   = _____

4. re + duce + ing   = _____

5. verse + ion   = _____

6. trans + fer   = _____

7. re + pel   = _____

8. heavy + est   = _____

9. in + cure + able   = _____

10. dis + ease   = _____

PART	A	B	C	D	E	F	G	H	Worksheet Errors	Worksheet Points	Oral Points	Bonus Points	Total Points
											+	+	=

Part A

1. _____ 5. _____
2. _____ 6. _____
3. _____ 7. _____
4. _____ 8. _____

Part B

1. _____
   _____
2. _____
   _____

Part C

1. _____ 5. _____
2. _____ 6. _____
3. _____ 7. _____
4. _____ 8. _____

Part D

1. show + en = _____
2. length + en = _____
3. blow + en = _____
4. sew + en = _____
5. prove + en = _____
6. know + en = _____
7. light + en = _____
8. grow + en = _____

Lesson 87

Part E

Draw a line from each word to its meaning.

sent •   • to make clothes

right •   • a thing that flies

tail •   • ordinary

sew •   • a story

cent •   • the end

whole •   • one hundred

write •   • moved somewhere

feat •   • doing something great

hole •   • the things you walk on

plane •   • correct

tale •   • putting words on paper

plain •   • all parts together

feet •   • an empty space

PART	A	B	C	D	E	F	G	H	Worksheet Errors	Worksheet Points	Oral Points	Bonus Points	Total Points
											+	+	=

Part A

1. _____   4. _____

2. _____   5. _____

3. _____   6. _____

Part B

1. _____   5. _____

2. _____   6. _____

3. _____   7. _____

4. _____   8. _____

Part C

Add the morphographs together. Remember to use your rule.

1. strength + en = _____

2. grow + en   = _____

3. straight + en = _____

4. wide + en   = _____

5. blow + en   = _____

6. know + en   = _____

7. mad + en   = _____

8. throw + en   = _____

Lesson 88

Part D

Circle the misspelled word in each group. Then write it correctly on the line.

1. qwart

   revision

   thirsty

   failure

   _____

2. basic

   quoteable

   dangerous

   reverse

   _____

3. breifly

   physical

   spinning

   scope

   _____

4. transplant

   photograph

   straight

   heavyness

   _____

5. requested

   thousand

   breth

   duties

   _____

6. worried

   showen

   cloudy

   pleasure

   _____

Part E

Make 11 real words from the morphographs in the box.

serve	con	fine	de	form	re	tain

1. _____

2. _____

3. _____

4. _____

5. _____

6. _____

7. _____

8. _____

9. _____

10. _____

11. _____

PART	A	B	C	D	E	F	G	H	Worksheet Errors	Worksheet Points	Oral Points	Bonus Points	Total Points
											+	+	=

Part A

1. _____
2. _____
3. _____
4. _____
5. _____

Part B

1. _____
2. _____
3. _____
4. _____
5. _____
6. _____
7. _____
8. _____

Part C

Add the morphographs together. Remember to use your rule.

1. blow + ing = _____
2. blow + en = _____
3. fresh + en = _____
4. sew + en = _____
5. sew + ed = _____
6. length + en = _____
7. grow + en = _____
8. throw + ing = _____

Lesson 89

Part D

Write **s** or **es** in the second column. Then add the morphographs together.

s or **es**

1. class   + _____ = _____
2. danger   + _____ = _____
3. progress   + _____ = _____

s or **es**

4. vary   + _____ = _____
5. box   + _____ = _____
6. story   + _____ = _____

Part E

Fill in the blanks to show the morphographs in each word.

1. _____ = reverse
2. _____ = version
3. _____ = revise
4. _____ = revision
5. _____ = injection
6. _____ = prefolded
7. _____ = formal
8. _____ = physical
9. _____ = cubic
10. _____ = cutest

PART	A	B	C	D	E	F	G	H	Worksheet Errors	Worksheet Points	Oral Points	Bonus Points	Total Points
											+	+	=

Part A

1. _____   4. _____

2. _____   5. _____

3. _____   6. _____

Part B

1. _____   5. _____

2. _____   6. _____

3. _____   7. _____

4. _____   8. _____

Part C

1. _____   4. _____

2. _____   5. _____

3. _____   6. _____

Part D

Circle the short **cvc** morphographs.

1. ship	4. boy	7. pel	10. slow	13. sew
2. tect	5. spirit	8. gress	11. shed	14. star
3. fer	6. box	9. cover	12. danger	

Part E

Complete each sentence correctly with one of these words:

right   plainly   various   tailing

1. I could understand you better if you would speak more _____ .

2. Unfortunately, he said the _____ thing, but at the wrong time.

3. Mr. Penn awarded points to _____ students in his class.

4. Free countries feature the _____ to vote.

5. Joe got into an accident because he was _____ the car in front of him too closely.

PART	A	B	C	D	E	F	G	H	Worksheet Errors	Worksheet Points	Oral Points	Bonus Points	Total Points
											+	+	=

Lesson 91

Part A

1. _____   4. _____
2. _____   5. _____
3. _____   6. _____

Part B

Underline any word that is misspelled and write it correctly in the right-hand column.

Some boyes were plaing a
frendly game of chanse.

_____

_____

Janie took a quik breth and
lifted the heavie boxes.

_____

_____

_____

_____

_____

Part C

Add the morphographs together. Remember to use your spelling rules.

1. sew + en   = _____

2. danger + ous   = _____

3. thirst + y + ness = _____

4. big + est   = _____

5. lone + ly + ness = _____

6. cube + ic   = _____

7. in + struct + ive + ly = _____

8. trans + fuse   = _____

9. trans + fuse + ion = _____

10. un + fashion + able = _____

11. con + verse + ion = _____

12. re + cover + able = _____

13. pro + vise + ion = _____

14. ex + pel   = _____

15. dis + please + ure = _____

146

Part D

These words are in the puzzle.
Circle 7 or more of the words.

shake   athlete   thousand   transact   scope

friend   seed   under   equal   voice   niece   farm

```
a t h s v o i c e
a t h l e t e a v
f s c o p e v s e
r a h v u n d e r
i t r a n s a c t
e v s m k f a e a
n i e c e e s n a
d n e e q u a l d
```

PART	A	B	C	D	E	F	G	H	Worksheet Errors	Worksheet Points	Oral Points	Bonus Points	Total Points
											+	+	=

Lesson 93

Part A

1. _____   4. _____
2. _____   5. _____
3. _____   6. _____

Part B

1. _____   5. _____
2. _____   6. _____
3. _____   7. _____
4. _____   8. _____

Part C

1. _____   5. _____
2. _____   6. _____
3. _____   7. _____
4. _____   8. _____

Part D

Underline any word that is misspelled and write it correctly in the right-hand column.

An unknoen athelete defeated
a famus runner.

_____

_____

I have progresed wonderfully in
my photagraphy class.

_____

_____

_____

_____

_____

Part E

Fill in the blanks to show the morphographs in each word.

1. _____ = objection

2. _____ = revise

3. _____ = vision

4. _____ = version

5. _____ = destructively

6. _____ = conversion

7. _____ = athletic

8. _____ = shaken

9. _____ = constructive

10. _____ = fashionable

11. _____ = basics

12. _____ = exception

PART	A	B	C	D	E	F	G	H	Worksheet Errors	Worksheet Points	Oral Points	Bonus Points	Total Points
											+	+	=

Lesson 94

Part A

1. _____
2. _____
3. _____

4. _____
5. _____
6. _____

Part B

1. _____
2. _____
3. _____

4. _____
5. _____
6. _____

Part C

Add these morphographs together.

1. ob + struct = _____
2. happy + ly = _____
3. trans + gress + ion = _____
4. muse + ic + al = _____
5. un + fashion + able = _____
6. re + fer = _____
7. settle + ment = _____
8. athlete + ic = _____
9. know + en = _____
10. mis + con + cept + ion = _____
11. physic + ist = _____
12. ship + ment = _____

Part D

Circle the misspelled word in each group. Then write it correctly on the line.

1. basic

   forgett

   transfusion

   distract

   _____

2. produce

   destruktive

   obtain

   deception

   _____

3. contract

   objective

   confuse

   transfir

   _____

4. reduse

   injecting

   regress

   content

   _____

5. dangerus

   repel

   contract

   graphic

   _____

Part E

Make 4 real words from the morphographs in the box.

Be careful. Only four real words are possible.

| re   mis   dis   pel   spell |

1. _____   3. _____

2. _____   4. _____

PART	A	B	C	D	E	F	G	H	Worksheet Errors	Worksheet Points	Oral Points	Bonus Points	Total Points
											+	+	=

Lesson 95

Part A

1. _____ 5. _____

2. _____ 6. _____

3. _____ 7. _____

4. _____

Part B

Add these morphographs together.

1. real + ly   = _____

2. hopeful + ly = _____

3. magic + ly   = _____

4. flat + ly   = _____

5. sure + ly   = _____

6. basic + ly   = _____

7. classic + ly = _____

8. equal + ly   = _____

Part C

Add these morphographs together.

1. settle + ment   = _____

2. verse + ion   = _____

3. con + struct + ion = _____

4. re + fer   = _____

5. re + duce + ing   = _____

6. re + pel   = _____

7. con + tain + er   = _____

8. pro + ject + ed   = _____

9. muse + ic   = _____

10. ease + y   = _____

152

Part D

Draw a line from each word to its meaning.

son •   • to plant

four •   • the end

sow •   • a thing that flies

sew •   • a male child

plane •   • putting words on paper

tale •   • one hundred

sent •   • a story

plain •   • all parts together

tail •   • to make clothes

cent •   • moved somewhere

write •   • the number 4

whole •   • ordinary

Part E

Fill in the blanks to show the morphographs in each word.

1. _____ = quarter

2. _____ = devise

3. _____ = thirsty

4. _____ = requesting

5. _____ = progressively

6. _____ = reverse

PART	A	B	C	D	E	F	G	H	Worksheet Errors	Worksheet Points	Oral Points	Bonus Points	Total Points
										+	+	=	

Lesson 96

Part A

1. _____ 4. _____

2. _____ 5. _____

3. _____ 6. _____

Part B

1. cute + ly   = _____

2. physic + ly = _____

3. faint + ly   = _____

4. heavy + ly   = _____

5. logic + ly   = _____

6. gainful + ly = _____

7. quick + ly   = _____

8. heroic + ly = _____

Part C

Add these morphographs together.

1. pro + pel   = _____

2. in + fect + ion   = _____

3. in + struct + ion   = _____

4. ob + struct   = _____

5. ob + ject   = _____

6. de + fect + ive   = _____

7. con + fer   = _____

8. trans + fer   = _____

9. heavy + ness   = _____

10. for + give + ing   = _____

11. quest + ion + able = _____

12. athlete + ic   = _____

Part D

Figure out the rules and write them.

1. a word when the word ends with a . . .the next morphograph begins . . .change the **y** to **i** in . . .with anything, except **i** . . .consonant-and-**y** and

_____

_____

2. next morphograph begins with **v** . . .word ends **cvc** and the . . .in a short word when the . . .double the final **c**

_____

_____

Part E

Circle the short **cvc** morphographs.

1. wander	4. fect	7. hop	10. tain
2. shed	5. bar	8. ship	11. pel
3. sew	6. bit	9. fer	12. poison

PART	A	B	C	D	E	F	G	H	Worksheet Errors	Worksheet Points	Oral Points	Bonus Points	Total Points
											+	+	=

Lesson 97

Part A

1. _____ 4. _____

2. _____ 5. _____

3. _____ 6. _____

Part B

Add the morphographs together. Remember to use the rule about adding **al** before **ly**.

1. live + ly   = _____

2. graphic + ly   = _____

3. friendly + ness = _____

4. base + ment   = _____

5. transform + er = _____

6. chief + ly   = _____

7. artistic + ly = _____

8. glory + ous   = _____

Part C

1. _____ 5. _____

2. _____ 6. _____

3. _____ 7. _____

4. _____ 8. _____

Part D

Write **s** or **es** in the second column. Then add the morphographs together.

s or **es**

1. reason   + _____ = _____

2. class   + _____ = _____

3. brush   + _____ = _____

4. baby   + _____ = _____

5. box   + _____ = _____

6. copy   + _____ = _____

7. fashion   + _____ = _____

8. rich   + _____ = _____

Part E

Fill in the blanks to show the morphographs in each word.

1. _____ = courting

2. _____ = living

3. _____ = basement

4. _____ = cubic

5. _____ = contend

6. _____ = pertain

7. _____ = compression

8. _____ = around

9. _____ = apart

10. _____ = transaction

PART	A	B	C	D	E	F	G	H	Worksheet Errors	Worksheet Points	Oral Points	Bonus Points	Total Points
											+	+	=

Lesson 98

Part A

1. _____ 4. _____

2. _____ 5. _____

3. _____ 6. _____

Part B

1. _____ 5. _____

2. _____ 6. _____

3. _____ 7. _____

4. _____ 8. _____

Part C

Add the morphographs together. Remember to use the rule about adding **al** before **ly**.

1. ship + ment = _____

2. observe + ing = _____

3. classic + ly = _____

4. bid + ing = _____

5. profuse + ly = _____

6. basic + ly = _____

7. detect + ion = _____

8. define + ing = _____

Part D

1. _____

_____

2. _____

_____

Part E

Circle the misspelled word in each group. Then write it correctly on the line.

1. widely
   equaly
   unchanged
   strength

   _____

2. pushyness
   athletic
   heavily
   basic

   _____

3. thousand
   fashion
   version
   cheif

   _____

4. photograph
   vishun
   breathless
   spirit

   _____

5. rezerve
   dutiful
   request
   quoted

   _____

6. straight
   explain
   hopefully
   throwen

   _____

PART	A	B	C	D	E	F	G	H	Worksheet Errors	Worksheet Points	Oral Points	Bonus Points	Total Points
											+	+	=

Lesson 99

Part A

Study these words on your own. There will be a test on these words during your next spelling lesson.

dim	star	mud	blot	bed
hid	rob	grab	bug	leg

Part B

1. _____   7. _____
2. _____   8. _____
3. _____   9. _____
4. _____   10. _____
5. _____   11. _____
6. _____   12. _____

Part C

1. _____   5. _____
2. _____   6. _____
3. _____   7. _____
4. _____   8. _____

Part D

Add the morphographs together. Remember to use the rule about adding **al** before **ly**.

1. physic + ly = _____   5. flat + ly   = _____
2. hopeful + ly = _____   6. thirst + y = _____
3. basic + ly = _____   7. count + ing = _____
4. live + ing = _____   8. class + es = _____

Part E

Add these morphographs together.

1. star + less = _____   6. grab + ing = _____
2. rob + er   = _____   7. mud + y   = _____
3. hid + en   = _____   8. leg + s   = _____
4. dim + ly   = _____   9. blot + ed = _____
5. bed + s   = _____   10. bug + s   = _____

PART	A	B	C	D	E	F	G	H	Worksheet Errors	Worksheet Points	Oral Points	Bonus Points	Total Points
											+	+	=

160

Part A

1. _____ 4. _____
2. _____ 5. _____
3. _____ 6. _____

Part B

1. _____ 6. _____
2. _____ 7. _____
3. _____ 8. _____
4. _____ 9. _____
5. _____ 10. _____

Part C

1. _____ 5. _____
2. _____ 6. _____
3. _____ 7. _____
4. _____ 8. _____

Part D

Add the morphographs together. Remember to use the rule about adding **al** before **ly**.

1. thousand + s = _____   5. forgetful + ly = _____
2. quick + ly = _____   6. athletic + ly = _____
3. hop + er = _____   7. push + y = _____
4. logic + ly = _____   8. run + ing = _____

Part E

Complete each sentence correctly with one of these words:

fore   sewn   plainly   son   sow

1. Mr. Morgan's oldest _____ is a nurse.

2. Everyone moved to the _____ of the ship.

3. Several farmers _____ their wheat before winter.

4. All Marcy's clothes are _____ by hand.

5. On a clear day, three mountains are _____ visible from Spencer's Creek.

6. The woman in the next apartment treats me like her own _____ .

PART	A	B	C	D	E	F	G	H	Worksheet Errors	Worksheet Points	Oral Points	Bonus Points	Total Points
											+	+	=

Lesson 101

Part A

1. _____   4. _____
2. _____   5. _____
3. _____

Part B

	plural word			**plural word**
1. thief:	_____		3. loaf:	_____
2. wife:	_____		4. wolf:	_____

Part C

1. _____   5. _____
2. _____   6. _____
3. _____   7. _____
4. _____   8. _____

Part D

These words are in the puzzle.

Circle 9 or more of the words.

government   graphic   thousand   heroic

sort   tend   danger   wonder   spend

cement   alike   ground   shine   voters

```
g  t  t  w  c  s  h  i  n  e
g  h  t  g  o  e  p  g  t  c
g  o  v  e  r  n  m  e  n  t
r  u  c  o  n  a  d  e  n  e
o  s  o  r  t  d  p  e  n  d
u  a  l  i  k  e  r  h  r  t
n  n  c  c  h  e  r  o  i  c
d  d  a  n  g  e  r  s  m  c
```

Part E

Fill in the blanks to show the morphographs in each word.

1. _____ = famous

2. _____ = exposure

3. _____ = structure

4. _____ = across

5. _____ = describe

6. _____ = infamous

7. _____ = texture

8. _____ = example

9. _____ = progressively

10. _____ = structural

11. _____ = factually

12. _____ = complain

13. _____ = perceptive

14. _____ = obstruction

15. _____ = around

PART	A	B	C	D	E	F	G	H	Worksheet Errors	Worksheet Points	Oral Points	Bonus Points	Total Points
											+	+	=

Lesson 103

Part A

1. _____ 5. _____

2. _____ 6. _____

3. _____ 7. _____

4. _____ 8. _____

Part B

1. wolf: _____ 3. half: _____

2. wife: _____ 4. shelf: _____

Part C

Write each of these words in a box. Write "free space" in one box.

across	infected	request	starry	govern
range	spirit	describe	recover	speechless
settle	sleepless	pretend	reasonable	thief

Part D

Make 11 real words from the morphographs in the box.

| ob   ed   ject   pro   ion   in   de |

1. _____ 7. _____

2. _____ 8. _____

3. _____ 9. _____

4. _____ 10. _____

5. _____ 11. _____

6. _____

PART	A	B	C	D	E	F	G	H	Worksheet Errors	Worksheet Points	Oral Points	Bonus Points	Total Points
											+	+	=

Part A

1. _____

_____

2. _____

_____

Part B

1. shelf _____ 3. calf: _____

2. loaf: _____ 4. thief: _____

Part C

1. _____ 4. _____

2. _____ 5. _____

3. _____ 6. _____

Part D

Circle the short **cvc** morphographs.

1. grab	4. cur	7. mud	10. pel	13. state
2. mit	5. tend	8. fer	11. ship	14. shed
3. long	6. reason	9. coat	12. poison	15. logic

Part E

Fill in the blanks to show the morphographs in each word.

1. _____ = factual

2. _____ = unusual

3. _____ = alike

4. _____ = living

5. _____ = muddy

6. _____ = vision

7. _____ = visual

8. _____ = confinement

9. _____ = transaction

10. _____ = pushiness

PART	A	B	C	D	E	F	G	H	Worksheet Errors	Worksheet Points	Oral Points	Bonus Points	Total Points
											+	+	=

Part A

1. _____
2. _____
3. _____
4. _____

5. _____
6. _____
7. _____
8. _____

Part B

1. _____
2. _____
3. _____

4. _____
5. _____
6. _____

Part C

1. basic + ly   = _____
2. impose + ing = _____
3. love + ly   = _____
4. athletic + ly = _____
5. critic + ly = _____
6. faint + ly   = _____

Part D

Draw a line from each word to its meaning.

son •   • one hundred

four •   • in front of

sew •   • to plant

fore •   • to make clothes

sow •   • the end

tale •   • a male child

tail •   • ordinary

plain •   • the number 4

cent •   • a story

sent •   • moved somewhere

Part E

Add the morphographs together.

1. mud + y = _____

2. ease + y + ly = _____

3. lone + ly + ness = _____

4. dim + ly = _____

5. choose + ing = _____

6. type + ic + al = _____

7. re + late + ive = _____

8. vise + ual + ly = _____

PART	A	B	C	D	E	F	G	H	Worksheet Errors	Worksheet Points	Oral Points	Bonus Points	Total Points
											+	+	=

Lesson 106

Part A

1. _____   5. _____
2. _____   6. _____
3. _____   7. _____
4. _____   8. _____

Part B

1. grow + en = _____   5. straight + en = _____
2. sweet + en = _____   6. bit + en   = _____
3. act + ual = _____   7. sew + en   = _____
4. blow + en = _____   8. know + ing = _____

Part C

1. _____   4. _____
2. _____   5. _____
3. _____   6. _____

Part D

Write the plural for each word. Remember to say the plural word to yourself.

1. calf: _____   3. shelf: _____
2. life: _____   4. wolf: _____

Part E

Complete each sentence correctly with one of these words:

tales   sent   four   plain   sew

1. John can_____ better than his sister Lil.

2. My father used to read us fairy _____ at bedtime.

3. Sue likes her tea with cream and sugar, I like mine _____ .

4. I have to _____ a button on to my coat before I can go out.

5. Jenny's uncle _____ her a fishing rod for her birthday.

6. A box has _____ sides, a top, and a bottom.

Part A

1. _____

2. _____

3. _____

4. _____

5. _____

6. _____

Part B

Study these words on your own. There will be a test on these words during your next spelling lesson.

hit	spot	frog	rat	chin
trip	ton	gun	net	pig

Part C

1. _____

2. _____

3. _____

4. _____

5. _____

6. _____

7. _____

8. _____

Part D

1. _____

2. _____

3. _____

4. _____

5. _____

6. _____

7. _____

8. _____

Part E

Write the plural for each word. Remember to say the plural word to yourself.

1. knife: _____

2. loaf: _____

3. life: _____

4. self: _____

Part F

Fill in the blanks to show the morphographs in each word.

1. _____ = describe

2. _____ = around

3. _____ = ascribe

4. _____ = belong

5. _____ = prevent

6. _____ = invention

7. _____ = converge

8. _____ = critical

9. _____ = permit

10. _____ = defective

PART	A	B	C	D	E	F	G	H	Worksheet Errors	Worksheet Points	Oral Points	Bonus Points	Total Points
										+	+	=	

Part A

1. _____ 4. _____

2. _____ 5. _____

3. _____ 6. _____

Part B

1. _____ 6. _____

2. _____ 7. _____

3. _____ 8. _____

4. _____ 9. _____

5. _____ 10. _____

Part C

1. _____

_____

2. _____

_____

Part D

Write the plural for each word. Remember to say the plural word to yourself.

1. wife: _____ 4. thief: _____

2. loaf: _____ 5. self: _____

3. life: _____ 6. wolf: _____

Part E

Add the morphographs together.

1. your + self = _____ 6. double + y = _____

2. de + scribe + ing = _____ 7. ob + ject + ive = _____

3. pro + pose + ed = _____ 8. trans + act + ion = _____

4. room + y + ness = _____ 9. spot + ed = _____

5. net + ed = _____ 10. con + sist = _____

PART	A	B	C	D	E	F	G	H	Worksheet Errors	Worksheet Points	Oral Points	Bonus Points	Total Points
											+	+	=

Lesson 109

Part A

1. _____
2. _____
3. _____
4. _____
5. _____
6. _____

Part B

1. _____
2. _____
3. _____
4. _____
5. _____
6. _____
7. _____
8. _____

Part C

1. _____
2. _____
3. _____
4. _____
5. _____
6. _____

Part D

Circle the misspelled word in each group. Then write it correctly on the line.

1. magic
   fashun
   shedding
   thieves

   _____

2. athalete
   thousands
   retain
   instructive

   _____

3. statement
   recover
   cheifly
   version

   _____

4. consept
   reduce
   request
   fried

   _____

5. deceptive
   various
   heavily
   maddness

   _____

6. winner
   berries
   thrown
   basicly

   _____

172

Part E

Fill in the blank to show the morphographs in each word.

1. _____ = subject

2. _____ = improvement

3. _____ = families

4. _____ = insisted

5. _____ = became

6. _____ = pretended

7. _____ = around

8. _____ = amusement

9. _____ = music

10. _____ = apartment

Part F

Figure out the rule and write it.

word ends **cvc** and the . . .in a short word when the . . .next morphograph begins with **v** . . .double the final **c**

_____

_____

PART	A	B	C	D	E	F	G	H	Worksheet Errors	Worksheet Points	Oral Points	Bonus Points	Total Points
											+	+	=

February 2, 1965

Dear Hank,

   I got the pet lizard you cent me. Thank you vary

much. Woold you believe that the little fellow has begun

snaping at people? My aunt was plaing with the lizard last

nite. Her fase was close to the little thing. All at once the

lizard jumpped up and bit her rite on the nose. Luckyly,

the bite was not bad. She washed her face with plane

water. She did'nt have a mark on her face, so you no the

bite realy wasn't bad.

   Thanks again for the unuseual pet.

                Your Frend,

                Emory

PART	A	B	C	D	E	F	G	H	Worksheet Errors	Worksheet Points	Oral Points	Bonus Points	Total Points
											+	+	=

Part A

1. _____
2. _____
3. _____
4. _____

5. _____
6. _____
7. _____
8. _____

Part B

1. _____
2. _____
3. _____
4. _____
5. _____

6. _____
7. _____
8. _____
9. _____

Part C

Part D

Circle the short **cvc** morphographs.

1. run
2. port
3. bar

4. fer
5. danger
6. mit

7. ject
8. snap
9. shop

10. wander
11. cur
12. pel

Part E

Write the plural word. Remember to say the plural word to yourself.

1. knife: _____

2. wolf: _____

3. life: _____

4. shelf: _____

5. thief: _____

6. leaf: _____

7. calf: _____

8. wife: _____

Part F

Fill in the blanks to show the morphographs in each word.

1. _____ = refer

2. _____ = propel

3. _____ = commit

4. _____ = rerun

5. _____ = unsnap

6. _____ = concur

7. _____ = reinstate

8. _____ = families

PART	A	B	C	D	E	F	G	H	Worksheet Errors	Worksheet Points	Oral Points	Bonus Points	Total Points
											+	+	=

Part A

1. chief: _____   3. gulf: _____

2. thief: _____   4. wolf: _____

Part B

1. _____   6. _____

2. _____   7. _____

3. _____   8. _____

4. _____   9. _____

5. _____

Part C

Circle the short **cvc** morphographs.

1. feet   3. chin   5. struct   7. fer   9. pel

2. mit   4. cur   6. critic   8. tain   10. trip

Part D

Circle the misspelled word in each group. Then write it correctly on the line.

1. personal   2. perform   3. briefs

   basement   obtain   sobtract

   befour   calf   incur

   apart   classicaly   transmit

   _____   _____   _____

4. insist   5. chooze   6. compound

   convert   grabbing   gradual

   lively   womanhood   defekt

   knifes   danger   impression

   _____   _____   _____

PART	A	B	C	D	E	F	G	H	Worksheet Errors	Worksheet Points	Oral Points	Bonus Points	Total Points
											+	+	=

Lesson 113

Part A

1. _____
2. _____
3. _____

4. _____
5. _____

Part B

Study these words on your own. There will be a test on these words during your next spelling lesson.

red	bud	gas	top	hog
gum	pan	cut	car	

Part C

1. _____
2. _____
3. _____

4. _____
5. _____
6. _____

Part D

Fill in the blanks to show the morphographs in each word.

1. _____ = awhile
2. _____ = incurable
3. _____ = improve
4. _____ = subscribe
5. _____ = families
6. _____ = typical
7. _____ = subtracting
8. _____ = government
9. _____ = forceful
10. _____ = invert

Part E

Complete each sentence correclty with one of these words:

sonny   week   plain   write   whole

1. Jill visits her grandparents every month, Carlos visits his every _____ .

2. Mr. Wilson is not my father, although he always calls me _____ .

3. Jim ate the _____ pie, and now he is sick.

4. I must remember to _____ a thank you letter to my Aunt Chole.

5. Just give me a _____ and simple answer. I don't want any fanciful tales.

6. Next _____ is Kim's birthday party. Are you coming?

7. Lui is only four years old, but he already knows how to read and _____ .

PART	A	B	C	D	E	F	G	H	Worksheet Errors	Worksheet Points	Oral Points	Bonus Points	Total Points
											+	+	=

Lesson 114

Part A

1. _____ 3. _____

2. _____ 4. _____

Part B

1. _____ 6. _____

2. _____ 7. _____

3. _____ 8. _____

4. _____ 9. _____

5. _____

Part C

1 puff: _____ 3. half: _____

2. self: _____ 4. chief: _____

Part D

Add the morphographs together.

1. cure + able = _____

2. im + pure = _____

3. re + sub + mit = _____

4. e + vent + ual = _____

5. ad + just + ment = _____

6. govern + ment + al = _____

7. ex + ample + s = _____

8. un + reason + able = _____

9. family + es = _____

10. ply + able = _____

11. de + script + ive = _____

12. poison + ous = _____

PART	A	B	C	D	E	F	G	H	Worksheet Errors	Worksheet Points	Oral Points	Bonus Points	Total Points
											+	+	=

Part A

1. _____   4. _____

2. _____   5. _____

3. _____

Part B

1. _____   4. _____

2. _____   5. _____

3. _____   6. _____

Part C

1. _____   5. _____

2. _____   6. _____

3. _____   7. _____

4. _____   8. _____

Part D

Write the plural for each word. Remember to say the plural word to yourself.

1. leaf: _____   4. life: _____

2. calf: _____   5. thief: _____

3. chief: _____   6. safe: _____

Part E

Fill in the blanks to show the morphographs in each word.

1. _____ = incurable

2. _____ = typing

3. _____ = typical

4. _____ = reject

5. _____ = adjective

6. _____ = prevent

7. _____ = eventful

8. _____ = subscriber

9. _____ = department

10. _____ = glorious

PART	A	B	C	D	E	F	G	H	Worksheet Errors	Worksheet Points	Oral Points	Bonus Points	Total Points
											+	+	=

Lesson 116

Part A

1. _____   3. _____

2. _____

Part B

January 14, 1979

Dear Customer

    Are you spinding more time than you need to on nasty household jobs? I'm righting to infrom you that we are now produsing the most usefull home appliance ever made. The new E-Z Home Unit can do thousans of jobs in your home. It changes the sheets on your family beds. It replaces bad fuzes and protecs your house from burglars. It will water any plants that you have growing in your house. It also washs windows, serves your dinner, and cures bad breth. It comes packed in reuseable cardboard boxes. The E-Z Home Unit can easly be put together using the helpfull instrucshuns that come with each order.

    Please send us your order today.

                Sincerely,

                I.M. Selling

PART	A	B	C	D	E	F	G	H	Worksheet Errors	Worksheet Points	Oral Points	Bonus Points	Total Points
											+	+	=

Part A

1. _____
2. _____

3. _____
4. _____

Part B

1. _____
2. _____
3. _____

4. _____
5. _____
6. _____

Part C

1. _____ = relentless

2. _____ = incomplete

3. _____ = surround

4. _____ = explore

Part D

Underline any word that is misspelled and write it correctly in the right-hand column.

A spotted frog solved the
magicle puzzel.   _____

                                        _____

The theif compoundded his
troubles by loosing his gun.   _____

                                        _____

                                        _____

                                        _____

                                        _____

                                        _____

Part E

Add the morphographs together.

1. de + tect + ion = _____

2. pro + tect + ion = _____

3. re + act + ion = _____

4. in + vent + ion = _____

5. trans + gress + ion = _____

6. fact + ion + s = _____

7. tract + ion = _____

8. de + fect + ion = _____

9. vise + ion = _____

10. de + press + ion = _____

PART	A	B	C	D	E	F	G	H	Worksheet Errors	Worksheet Points	Oral Points	Bonus Points	Total Points
											+	+	=

Part A

	ion form?	**or** or **er** form
1. fact:	_____	_____
2. design:	_____	_____
3. invent:	_____	_____
4. act:	_____	_____
5. speak:	_____	_____
6. photograph:	_____	_____

Part B

1. _____   4. _____
2. _____   5. _____
3. _____   6. _____

Part C

Circle the short **cvc** morphographs.

1. snap   6. act
2. fer   7. critic
3. mark   8. cur
4. ship   9. ceive
5. pel   10. box

Part D

Circle the misspelled word in each group. Then write it correctly on the line.

1. other	2. pityful	3. fashion	4. basicly
whose	wrong	thief	brought
civul	dangerous	reson	science
woman	uncover	knives	critic
_____	_____	_____	_____

Part E

Add the morphographs together.

1. sup + pose = _____
2. ex + plore + ing = _____
3. com + plete + ly = _____
4. sur + face = _____
5. pro + mote + ion = _____
6. re + lent + less = _____
7. ad + vise = _____
8. re + sume + ed = _____
9. un + e + vent + ful = _____
10. puzzle + ing = _____

PART	A	B	C	D	E	F	G	H	Worksheet Errors	Worksheet Points	Oral Points	Bonus Points	Total Points
										+	+	=	

Part A

1. _____ 2. _____ 3. _____

Part B

	ion form?	**or** or **er** form
1. transgress:	_____	_____
2. plant:	_____	_____
3. project:	_____	_____
4. compress:	_____	_____
5. retain:	_____	_____
6. tract:	_____	_____

Part C

1. rerun + ing = _____
2. infer + ing = _____
3. hit + er = _____
4. disarm + ed = _____
5. commit + ed = _____
6. ship + ing = _____
7. detect + ive = _____
8. snap + y = _____

Lesson 119

Part D

Make 11 real words from the morphographs in the box.

ex	ion	press	re	im	ive	de

1. _____   7. _____

2. _____   8. _____

3. _____   9. _____

4. _____   10. _____

5. _____   11. _____

6. _____

Part E

1. in + sist + ing   = _____

2. ad + mit   = _____

3. pro + mote + ion   = _____

4. pre + sume   = _____

5. mot + ive   = _____

6. con + verse + ion   = _____

7. pre + vent + ion   = _____

8. un + re + solve + ed = _____

PART	A	B	C	D	E	F	G	H	Worksheet Errors	Worksheet Points	Oral Points	Bonus Points	Total Points
											+	+	=

Part A

	ion form?	**or** or **er** form
1. revise:	_____	_____
2. light:	_____	_____
3. invent:	_____	_____
4. instruct:	_____	_____
5. stretch:	_____	_____
6. contract:	_____	_____

Part B

Underline the morphograph that each word ends with. Then add the next morphograph.

1. admit + ed = _____
2. dispel + ing = _____
3. imbed + ing = _____
4. instruct + ive = _____
5. protect + ion = _____
6. big + est   = _____
7. recur + ing = _____
8. graph + ic = _____

Part C

1. _____ = profess
2. _____ = proceed

Lesson 120

Part D

Underline any word that is misspelled and write it correctly in the right-hand column.

We weren't impresed with the
lenthy speech the athour gave.

_____

_____

_____

The adventurors hopped to
discover hidden treasure,
but they faund nothing

_____

_____

_____

_____

_____

_____

Part E

Fill in the blanks to show the morphographs in each word.

1. _____ = promotion

2. _____ = reviewing

3. _____ = dissolve

4. _____ = vision

5. _____ = confess

6. _____ = concise

7. _____ = exceedingly

8. _____ = predict

9. _____ = consume

10. _____ = section

PART	A	B	C	D	E	F	G	H	Worksheet Errors	Worksheet Points	Oral Points	Bonus Points	Total Points
											+	+	=

Part A

1. _____ 4. _____

2. _____ 5. _____

3. _____

Part B

	ion form ?	**er** or **or** form
1. heavy:	_____	_____
2. vise:	_____	_____
3. invent:	_____	_____
4. misspell:	_____	_____
5. confess:	_____	_____
6. inject:	_____	_____

Part C

1. _____ 5. _____

2. _____ 6. _____

3. _____ 7. _____

4. _____ 8. _____

Part D

Underline the morphograph that each word ends with. Then add the next morphograph.

1. repel + ing = _____

2. perfect + ion = _____

3. remote + ly = _____

4. bliss + ful = _____

5. submit + ing = _____

6. spot + less = _____

7. compel + ing = _____

8. commit + ment = _____

Lesson 121

Part E

1. _____   4. _____

2. _____   5. _____

3. _____   6. _____

Part F

Add the morphographs together.

1. value + able   = _____

2. pre + dict + ion   = _____

3. de + sign +er   = _____

4. at + tract + ion   = _____

5. re + quest   = _____

6. quest + ion + able = _____

7. quiet + ly   = _____

8. at + tend + ed   = _____

9. di + vise + ion   = _____

10. sup + ply + es   = _____

PART	A	B	C	D	E	F	G	H	Worksheet Errors	Worksheet Points	Oral Points	Bonus Points	Total Points
											+	+	=

Part A

Study these words on your own. There will be a test on these words during Lesson 124.

set	up	pop	stir	sit
cap	frog	bat	tip	dig

Part B

1. _____
2. _____
3. _____
4. _____
5. _____
6. _____
7. _____
8. _____

Part C

If there is an i-o-n form of the word, write it in the second column.
If there is no i-o-n form, leave the second column blank.
In the last column, write the word with the morphograph o-r or e-r.

	ion form ?	**or** or **er** form
1. vise:	_____	_____
2. profess:	_____	_____
3. review:	_____	_____
4. contract:	_____	_____
5. perform:	_____	_____
6. protect:	_____	_____

Lesson 122

Part D

Underline the morphograph that each word ends with. Then add the next morphograph.

1. backpack + er = _____

2. joy + ous = _____

3. propel + ing = _____

4. emit + ing = _____

5. outfit + er = _____

6. refer + ed = _____

7. forget + ing = _____

8. unsnap + ed = _____

Part E

Fill in the blanks to show the morphographs in each word.

1. _____ = subverted

2. _____ = invert

3. _____ = conscience

4. _____ = exceed

5. _____ = implore

6. _____ = supported

7. _____ = reply

8. _____ = supplier

PART	A	B	C	D	E	F	G	H	Worksheet Errors	Worksheet Points	Oral Points	Bonus Points	Total Points
											+	+	=

Part A

1. _____ 2. _____ 3. _____

Part B

1. _____ 6. _____
2. _____ 7. _____
3. _____ 8. _____
4. _____ 9. _____
5. _____ 10. _____

Part C

1. _____ = dismiss
2. _____ = record
3. _____ = appointment

Part D

Underline the morphograph that each word ends with. Then add the next morphograph.

1. spot +y   = _____
2. transfer + ing = _____
3. propel + er   = _____
4. unstop + able = _____
5. overstep + ing = _____
6. commit + ment = _____

195

Lesson 124

Part E

Add the morphographs together.

1. dis + cord   = _____

2. ex + plore + ing = _____

3. re + lent + less = _____

4. com + plete + ly = _____

5. sup + ply + es   = _____

6. sur + face   = _____

7. dict + ate + ion = _____

8. beauty + ful + ly = _____

9. pro + ceed + ing = _____

10. race + ial   = _____

11. pre + cise + ion = _____

12. de + ceive + ed = _____

PART	A	B	C	D	E	F	G	H	Worksheet Errors	Worksheet Points	Oral Points	Bonus Points	Total Points
											+	+	=

Part A

1. _____   2. _____   3. _____

Part B

1. _____   2. _____   3. _____

4. _____   5. _____   6. _____

7. _____   8. _____   9. _____

10. _____

Part C

November 19, 1954

Dear Mr. Swiss,

We were happy to recieve your subscripshun to the Clock-of-the-Month Club. Your furst clock owt to arrive at your home within a weak. It is shaped like a spray can, and we are sure you will luv it. Each month, you will receive a new clock with a beautyful, original dezign. In the past, we have cent thouzunds of clocks that double as plantters, ships, wolfs, eyedroppers, and many other objecs.

These fashunable dezigns will surely add a touch of majic to any room, and they are usefull items to have for your famly.

If you like the Clock-of-the-Month, keep it. We will bill you. If you do'nt like it, send it back in the original packege within fore days.

Thank you for choozing the Clock-of-the-Month Club. Have you thougth about a subscription for a freind?

_____   _____

_____   _____

PART	A	B	C	D	E	F	G	H	Worksheet Errors	Worksheet Points	Oral Points	Bonus Points	Total Points
											+	+	=

Lesson 126

Part A

1. _____   4. _____

2. _____   5. _____

3. _____   6. _____

Part B

1. _____ = concern

2. _____ = magician

3. _____ = direct

Part C

Circle the short **cvc** morphographs.

1. stir   6. major   11. pel

2. sist   7. box   12. spin

3. play   8. fer   13. know

4. mit   9. ceive   14. reason

5. cur   10. cover   15. trap

Part D

Draw a line from each word to its meaning

week •   • correct

sew •   • a story

plain •   • happy

sent •   • to make clothes

tale •   • they own it

their •   • ordinary

marry •   • not strong

right •   • moved somewhere

weak •   • to become husband and wife

merry •   • seven days

Part E

Add the morphographs together.

1. part + ial + ly = _____

2. di + vise + ion = _____

3. ease + y = _____

4. major + ite + y = _____

5. con + fess + ion = _____

6. in + com + plete = _____

7. value + able = _____

8. ad + ject + ive = _____

9. govern + ment +al = _____

10. pro + ceed = _____

11. re + serve + ate + ion = _____

12. re + sign + ate + ion = _____

PART	A	B	C	D	E	F	G	H	Worksheet Errors	Worksheet Points	Oral Points	Bonus Points	Total Points
											+	+	=

Lesson 127

Part A

1. water + ed   = _____
2. mother + ly   = _____
3. permit + ing   = _____
4. critic + al   = _____
5. contain + er   = _____
6. major + ite + y = _____
7. cap + ed   = _____

Part B

June 30, 1961

Dear Sandy,

I realy like to recieve your letters. You always right about wonderrful advenchures. I had not knowen that there are poisonus snakes at the lake. Were'nt you and your famly in some danjer? I'll bet you were vary happy to return home.

I have been studing insects for a sciense project. Most people don't like insects, but think many of them are actualy bueatiful. I have been keeping abowt a thousend of them in my bedroom.

As your friend, I must tell you about one weekness in your letters. Your speling is pityful. I can barely read haf the words. I hope you will try to make fewer misstakes in your next letter.

Yours sincerely,

Pat

_____ _____
_____ _____
_____ _____
_____ _____
_____ _____
_____ _____
_____ _____
_____ _____
_____ _____

PART	A	B	C	D	E	F	G	H	Worksheet Errors	Worksheet Points	Oral Points	Bonus Points	Total Points
											+	+	=

Part A

1. _____   3. _____

2. _____   4. _____

Part B

1. infer + ing   = _____

2. unstop + able= _____

3. uncover + ed = _____

4. recur + ed   = _____

5. spirit + ual   = _____

6. stir + ing   = _____

Part C

Fill in the blanks to show the morphographs in each word.

1. _____ = valuable

2. _____ = rejection

3. _____ = eject

4. _____ = evaluate

5. _____ = concern

6. _____ = divide

7. _____ = direction

8. _____ = appoint

9. _____ = improvement

10. _____ = approval

11. _____ = around

12. _____ = noted

13. _____ = notable

14. _____ = record

15. _____ = prediction

Lesson 128

Part D

These words are in the puzzle.

Circle 9 or more of the words.

receive	sect	settle	sure	serve
beauty	their	trouble	spotted	
tension	double	taken	stir	week

```
d  o  u  b  l  e  r
s  t  h  e  i  r  e
s  p  s  a  d  s  c
t  r  o  u  b  l  e
s  e  c  t  r  w  i
e  e  n  y  t  e  v
r  s  t  s  e  e  e
v  t  t  t  i  k  d
e  i  s  e  l  o  i
s  r  t  a  k  e  n
```

Part E

Add the morphographs together. Remember to use your spelling rules.

1. tense + ion = _____

2. pro + cess = _____

3. com + plete + ion = _____

4. con + dense + ate + ion = _____

5. beauty + ful + ly = _____

6. ad + verse + ite + y = _____

7. inter + cept + ion = _____

8. dig + ing = _____

9. ease + y + ly = _____

10. face + ial = _____

11. un + use + ual = _____

12. heavy + est = _____

PART	A	B	C	D	E	F	G	H	Worksheet Errors	Worksheet Points	Oral Points	Bonus Points	Total Points
											+	+	=

Part A

1. expel + ing = _____

2. poison + ous= _____

3. project + ion = _____

4. combat + ed = _____

5. wonder + ful = _____

6. dig + er = _____

Part B

1. _____ 5. _____

2. _____ 6. _____

3. _____ 7. _____

4. _____ 8. _____

Part C

Fill in the blanks to show the morphographs in each word.

1. _____ = remote

2. _____ = active

3. _____ = motive

4. _____ = motivate

5. _____ = motivation

6. _____ = promotion

7. _____ = predict

8. _____ = dictate

9. _____ = dictation

10. _____ = densely

11. _____ = condense

12. _____ = condensation

Lesson 129

Part D

Complete each sentence correctly with one of these words:

married   their   merry   marry   there   weekly

1. Everyone at the celebration was in a _____ mood.

2. Terry's sisters invest nearly all _____ money.

3. I think Louie will _____ an athlete some day.

4. My desk is by a window, but I don't like it _____ .

5. How long have your parents been _____ ?

6. The teachers are going to discuss the talent show at _____ _____ meeting.

Part E

If there is an i-o-n form of the word, write it in the second column.
If there is no i-o-n form, leave the second column blank.
In the last column, write the word with the morphograph o-r or e-r.

ion form ?	**or** or **er** form
1. direct: _____	_____
2. inspect: _____	_____
3. review: _____	_____
4. dictate: _____	_____
5. propel: _____	_____
6. farm: _____	_____

PART	A	B	C	D	E	F	G	H	Worksheet Errors	Worksheet Points	Oral Points	Bonus Points	Total Points
											+	+	=

Part A

1. _____ 3. _____

2. _____ 4. _____

Part B

1. _____ + _____ = _____

2. _____ + _____ = _____

3. _____ + _____ = _____

4. _____ + _____ = _____

Part C

1. _____ 5. _____

2. _____ 6. _____

3. _____ 7. _____

4. _____ 8. _____

Part D

1. _____ = preparing

2. _____ = controlled

Part E

Fill in the blanks to show the morphographs in each word.

1. _____ = define

2. _____ = finite

3. _____ = infinite

4. _____ = infinity

5. _____ = commend

6. _____ = recommend

PART	A	B	C	D	E	F	G	H	Worksheet Errors	Worksheet Points	Oral Points	Bonus Points	Total Points
											+	+	=

Part A

1. _____   3. _____
2. _____   4. _____

Part B

1. _____ = elect
2. _____ = perturb

Part C

1. _____ + _____ = _____
2. _____ + _____ = _____
3. _____ + _____ = _____
4. _____ + _____ = _____

Part D

Add the morphographs together.

1. con + stant + ly = _____

2. pro + cess = _____

3. in + di + rect = _____

4. con + cern = _____

5. pro + ceed + ing = _____

6. re + pel = _____

7. ideal + ly = _____

8. grave + ite + y = _____

9. tense + ion = _____

10. e + value + ate + ion = _____

Part E

Circle the misspelled word in each group. Then write it correctly on the line.

1. nervous

   magicle

   dangerous

   critical

   _____

2. sciense

   majority

   shelves

   weren't

   _____

3. puzzling

   simple

   watch

   fancyest

   _____

4. container

   depression

   transport

   thoughtfullness

   _____

5. proclame

   human

   destructive

   reviewer

   _____

6. spoiled

   bilding

   reasonable

   berries

   _____

PART	A	B	C	D	E	F	G	H	Worksheet Errors	Worksheet Points	Oral Points	Bonus Points	Total Points
											+	+	=

Lesson 132

Part A

1. _____   5. _____

2. _____   6. _____

3. _____   7. _____

4. _____   8. _____

Part B

1. _____ = providing

2. _____ = beginner

Part C

1. _____ + _____ = _____

2. _____ + _____ = _____

3. _____ + _____ = _____

4. _____ + _____ = _____

Part D

Add the morphographs together. Remember to use your spelling rules.

1. base + ic + ly   = _____

2. medic + ly   = _____

3. beauty + ful   = _____

4. scarce + ite + y   = _____

5. con + trol + ing   = _____

6. per + mit + ed   = _____

7. pro + fess + ion   = _____

8. di + vise + ion   = _____

9. pity + ful   = _____

10. real + ize + ate + ion = _____

208

Part E

Underline any word that is misspelled and write it correctly in the right-hand column.

1. Marty's family has a beautyful
    home with a vue of the lake.

    _____

    _____

2. I'm hopping for a good night's
    sleep because I have to give a
    speach tomorrow.

    _____

    _____

    _____

    _____

    _____

    _____

PART	A	B	C	D	E	F	G	H	Worksheet Errors	Worksheet Points	Oral Points	Bonus Points	Total Points
											+	+	=

Lesson 133

Part A

1. _____ 3. _____
2. _____ 4. _____

Part B

1. _____ 5. _____
2. _____ 6. _____
3. _____ 7. _____
4. _____ 8. _____

Part C

1. _____ + _____ = _____
2. _____ + _____ = _____
3. _____ + _____ = _____
4. _____ + _____ = _____

Part D

1. _____ = medicine
2. _____ = backward

Part E

Add the morphographs together.

1. se + pare + ate   = _____
2. cave + ite + y   = _____
3. real + ize + ate + ion = _____
4. in + di + rect + ly   = _____
5. e + lect + ion   = _____
6. part + ial + ly   = _____
7. in + tense + ite + y = _____
8. sane + ite + ate + ion = _____
9. un + author + ize + ed = _____
10. se + lect + ion   = _____

PART	A	B	C	D	E	F	G	H	Worksheet Errors	Worksheet Points	Oral Points	Bonus Points	Total Points
											+	+	=

Part A

1. _____   2. _____   3. _____

Part B

1. _____   5. _____

2. _____   6. _____

3. _____   7. _____

4. _____   8. _____

Part C

1. _____   5. _____

2. _____   6. _____

3. _____   7. _____

4. _____   8. _____

Part D

1. _____ = forbidden

Part E

Fill in the blanks to show the morphographs in each word.

1. _____ = refine

2. _____ = prepare

3. _____ = finite

4. _____ = forward

5. _____ = preparation

6. _____ = separate

7. _____ = medical

8. _____ = separation

9. _____ = medicine

10. _____ = completely

PART	A	B	C	D	E	F	G	H	Worksheet Errors	Worksheet Points	Oral Points	Bonus Points	Total Points
											+	+	=

Lesson 135

Part A

1. _____
2. _____
3. _____

Part B

1. _____ = forgotten
2. _____ = desirous

Part C

Add the morphographs together. Remember to use your spelling rules.

1. for + bid + en   = _____
2. dis + miss + al   = _____
3. un + con + trol + ed   = _____
4. ac + cent + ed   = _____
5. re + cur + ing   = _____
6. real + ize + ate + ion = _____
7. beauty + ful + ly   = _____
8. pro + pel + er   = _____
9. com + mit +ment   = _____
10. un + com + mit + ed   = _____
11. grave + ite + y   = _____
12. note + ice + ing   = _____

Part D

Underline any word that is misspelled and write it correctly in the right-hand column.

We will autherize the contract for
the construshion of the medicle building.

_____

_____

The idealist was'nt vary reelistic
about planing her afternoon.

_____

_____

You can win most ellections with a
majoritee of the votes.

_____

_____

_____

_____

_____

_____

Part E

If there is an i-o-n form of the word, write it in the second column.
If there is no i-o-n form, leave the second column blank.
In the last column, write the word with the morphograph o-r or e-r.

	ion form ?	**or** or **er** form
1. collect:		
2. supervise:		
3. report:		
4. profess:		
5. dictate:		
6. detect:		

PART	A	B	C	D	E	F	G	H	Worksheet Errors	Worksheet Points	Oral Points	Bonus Points	Total Points
											+	+	=

Lesson 136

Part A

1. _____ = sociable

2. _____ = exhilarate

Part B

1. _____   2. _____

Part C

1. _____
_____

2. _____
_____

Part D

1. _____   4. _____

2. _____   5. _____

3. _____   6. _____

Part E

Draw a line from each word to its meaning.

their •   • all parts together

marry •   • not strong

right •   • they own it

weak •   • putting words on paper

there •   • to become husband and wife

write •   • happy

plain •   • they are

whole •   • correct

merry •   • in that place

they're •   • ordinary

Part A

1. _____   5. _____
2. _____   6. _____
3. _____   7. _____
4. _____   8. _____

Part B

1. _____   4. _____
2. _____   5. _____
3. _____   6. _____

Part C

Make 15 real words from the morphographs in the box.

un	ate	vent	ion	able	pre	dict	or	in

1. _____   9. _____
2. _____   10. _____
3. _____   11. _____
4. _____   12. _____
5. _____   13. _____
6. _____   14. _____
7. _____   15. _____
8. _____

Part D

Fill in the blanks to show the morphographs in each word.

1. _____ = realization
2. _____ = decreasing
3. _____ = partially
4. _____ = designation
5. _____ = condensation
6. _____ = civilization
7. _____ = dismiss
8. _____ = admission
9. _____ = sociable
10. _____ = hilarity

Lesson 137

Part E

Add the morphographs together.

1. in + quire + y   = _____

2. ex + hilar + ate   = _____

3. magic + ian   = _____

4. un + dis + pute + ed   = _____

5. com + pro + mise   = _____

6. intro + duct + ion   = _____

7. ap + ply + es   = _____

8. at + tend + ed   = _____

9. sur + round + ing + s   = _____

10. de + fine + ite + ly   = _____

11. marry + age   = _____

12. re + com + mend + ed   = _____

PART	A	B	C	D	E	F	G	H	Worksheet Errors	Worksheet Points	Oral Points	Bonus Points	Total Points
											+	+	=

Part A

1. _____   5. _____
2. _____   6. _____
3. _____   7. _____
4. _____   8. _____

Part B

1. _____   4. _____
2. _____   5. _____
3. _____   6. _____

Part C

Add the morphographs together. Remember to use your spelling rules.

1. base + ic + ly   = _____
2. grave + ite + y   = _____
3. be + gin + er   = _____
4. per + mit + ed   = _____
5. friend + ly + ness   = _____
6. di + vide   = _____
7. know + en   = _____
8. se +pare + ate + ion = _____
9. govern + ment + al   = _____
10. a + cross   = _____
11. athlete + ic + ly   = _____
12. vary + ous   = _____

Part D

Fill in the blanks to show the morphographs in each word.

1. _____ = permitting

2. _____ = refinement

3. _____ = finally

4. _____ = business

5. _____ = indefinite

6. _____ = expensive

7. _____ = accurate

8. _____ = uncurable

Part E

Complete each sentence correctly with one of these words:

they're   right   their   there   write

1. Mark put my skateboard in the garage, but I didn't want it _____ .

2. After Lee and Tony's party, _____ going to clean the house themselves.

3. What do you call people who can _____ equally well with _____ left hand or _____ hand?

4. My dogs spread _____ toys all over the kitchen floor.

PART	A	B	C	D	E	F	G	H	Worksheet Errors	Worksheet Points	Oral Points	Bonus Points	Total Points
										+	+	=	

Part A

1. _____   5. _____
2. _____   6. _____
3. _____   7. _____
4. _____   8. _____

Part B

Underline any word that is misspelled and write it correctly in the right-hand column.

The professer has a busness
that is seperate from her
teaching.

_____

_____

J.P. found inexpensuve transportation
for having his equipment transfered
to his new office.

_____

_____

_____

_____

_____

_____

Part C

Figure out the rules and write them.

1. from a word when the . . . vowel letter . . . drop the **e** . . . next morphograph begins with a

_____

_____

2. and the next morphograph begins with anything, . . . when the word ends with a consonant-and-**y** . . . except **i** . . . change

   the **y** to **i** in a word

_____

_____

Part D

Add the morphographs together.

1. image + ine = _____

2. soci + al = _____

3. nine + teen = _____

4. civil + ize + ate + ion = _____

5. un + fashion + able = _____

6. image + ine + ate + ion = _____

7. intro +duct + ion = _____

8. dis + re + pute + able = _____

9. muse + ic + ian = _____

10. com + mend + able = _____

11. inter + miss + ion = _____

12. pro + verb + ial = _____

PART	A	B	C	D	E	F	G	H	Worksheet Errors	Worksheet Points	Oral Points	Bonus Points	Total Points
											+	+	=

Section A Bases introduced in Lessons 1-13

quiet	1	brush	2	take	6	human	8
fresh	1	spell	3	author	6	stretch	8
born	1	back	3	motor	6	catch	8
pack	1	thick	3	help	6	dull	8
wonder	1	happy	3	grand	7	press	9
spend	1	match	4	friend	7	form	9
light	2	port	4	sell	7		
crash	2	sort	4	fill	7		

Section B Some words made from morphographs taught through Lesson 13

author	grand	motoring	selling
authoring	grandest	pack	sort
back	grandness	port	sorting
backless	happy	portable	spell
born	help	press	spelling
brush	helpless	quiet	spend
catch	helplessness	quietest	spendable
catching	human	quietness	stretch
crash	humanness	reborn	stretching
dull	light	refill	take
dullest	lightest	refillable	thick
dullness	lightness	reform	thickest
fill	match	refresh	thickness
filling	matching	refreshing	unborn
form	matchless	rematch	unhappy
forming	mismatch	repack	unpack
formless	misspell	report	unrefillable
fresh	misspending	repress	unrefreshing
freshest	mistake	resellable	wonder
friend	motor	sell	wondering

Appendix B

Section A Bases introduced in Lessons 14-23

like	14	use	15	trace	17	equal	20
fine	14	rest	16	face	17	hate	20
name	14	dine	16	cent	17	farm	20
note	14	serve	16	snap	19	cart	20
right	15	care	16	mad	19	arm	20
night	15	bare	16	sad	19	bar	20
grade	15	bliss	17	swim	19		
wide	15	city	17	shop	19		
hope	15	rent	17	run	19		

Section B Rules introduced in Lessons 14-23

Final E Rule (Lesson 14) "When a word ends in **e** and you add a morphograph that begins with a vowel letter, drop the **e**."

Section C Some words made of morphographs taught through Lesson 23

arm	fine	note	sadness
armed	finely	packer	sadly
armless	fineness	prepacked	serve
authored	former	preserve	shop
backer	friendly	prestretched	snap
backpacker	grade	quietly	stretchable
bar	grander	recent	stretcher
bare	hate	refine	swim
barely	hope	reformed	trace
bliss	hopelessly	refreshing	unequal
brushed	humanly	rematch	unequally
care	lightly	rename	unfarmable
carelessly	likable	rent	unfriendly
carelessness	like	renter	ungraded
cart	likeness	reported	unlikely
carted	mad	repressed	unpacked
catcher	madness	rerun	unrented
cent	mismatched	reserve	unrest
city	misspelled	rest	unsnap
dine	misspelling	restlessly	usable
equal	mistake	restlessness	use
equally	misuse	retrace	uselessness
face	name	reuse	wide
faceless	nameless	right	widely
farm	namely	rightly	wondered
farmer	night	run	
filler	notable	sad	

Section A Bases introduced in Lessons 24-35

race	24	stop	25	deal	28	world	30
force	24	wash	27	lone	28	step	30
choice	24	water	27	clan	28	drop	30
voice	24	want	27	sign	29	shine	30
coil	24	wander	27	length	29	play	32
plan	24	nerve	27	strength	29	boy	32
change	25	pass	27	hot	29	joy	32
page	25	verb	28	big	29	civil	32
rage	25	herb	28	lose	29	berry	32
cage	25	real	28	work	30		

Section B Rules introduced in Lessons 24-35

Doubling Rule (Lesson 25) "When a short word ends **cvc** and the next morphograph begins with a **v,** double the final **c.**"

Vowel-Consonant (Lesson 32) "**Y** at the end of a morphograph is a vowel letter. The vowels are **a, e, i, o, u,** and **y** at the end of a morphograph."

Section C Some words made from morphographs taught through Lesson 35

barely	deal	forcefully	liked	plan	resign	uncaged	want
bareness	dealer	formal	likely	play	resigning	unchanging	wash
barest	defacing	freshener	liken	playful	rested	uncivil	washer
berry	defining	hateful	likeness	portable	restful	uncoiled	water
big	deform	hating	likening	prewashed	resting	undefinable	widely
blissful	degrade	helpfulness	liking	quietest	restless	unlikable	widen
boy	delighted	herb	lone	quietly	rightfully	unmistakable	wideness
boyish	delightful	herbal	lonely	quietness	shine	unnerving	widening
boyishness	denoting	hoped	lose	race	shining	unplayable	widest
cage	departed	hopeful	loser	racer	sign	unreal	work
cageless	depressing	hopeless	misstep	rage	signal	unreserved	workable
cared	deserved	hoping	mistaken	raging	signed	unwanted	worker
careful	designer	hot	nerve	real	signing	usable	world
careless	dining	hotter	notable	really	step	usage	worldly
caring	drop	hottest	noted	recoil	stop	used	wonderful
change	equip	human	noting	redealing	strength	useful	
choice	faced	joy	packaging	redefine	stretchable	using	
choicest	final	joyful	page	refinable	stretched	verb	
civil	finely	joyless	pageless	refreshen	stretching	verbally	
civilly	fineness	length	paging	renamed	taken	voice	
clan	finest	lengthening	pass	rental	taking	voicing	
coil	force	likable	passage	replay	thicken	wander	

Appendix D

Section A Bases introduced in Lessons 36-46

study	36	baby	38	try	41	have	42
pity	36	wrong	38	late	41	carry	43
copy	36	wrap	38	fit	41	rise	43
nasty	36	buzz	38	should	41	mother	43
cry	36	fuzz	38	would	41	brother	43
dry	36	write	38	could	41	are	43
fancy	37	busy	40	story	42	were	43
sturdy	37	worry	40	safe	42	does	43
fur	37	fox	40	trap	42		
hurry	37	box	40	might	42		
fuse	37	tax	40	she	42		

Section B Rules introduced in Lessons 36-46

Y to I Rule (Lesson 36) "Change the **y** to **i** when a word ends with a consonant-and-**y**, and the next morphograph begins with anything, except i."

Plural Variation (Lesson 38) "If a word ends in **s, z, sh,** or **ch,** you add **es** to make the plural."

Plural Variation (Lesson 41) "If a word ends in **s, z, sh, ch** or **x,** you add **es** to make the plural. The letter **x** acts like two consonant letters."

Section C Some words made from morphographs taught through Lesson 46

are	carry	designers	having	motherless	restful	snapper	trying
baby	carrying	dined	hopeful	motors	restfully	snapping	unequal
babyish	catches	diner	hopefully	nasty	resting	snaps	unfit
backs	changes	dining	hopeless	package	restless	sorts	uninformed
baggage	clannish	confined	hopelessly	packaged	restlessly	stepped	unsturdy
bagged	confined	dropper	hurry	packaging	rests	stepping	unwrap
bagging	confines	dry	hurrying	packed	restudy	steps	usage
bared	conform	drying	inborn	packer	rewrap	stopped	useful
barer	confuse	equals	inform	packing	rights	stopper	usefully
baring	confusing	fancy	informally	passages	rise	stopping	useless
barred	connote	finals	informer	passes	rising	story	uselessly
bigger	conserve	finer	inhuman	pity	runner	stretched	user
biggest	consign	fining	instep	pitying	sadder	stretcher	using
box	copy	fit	intake	planning	saddest	stretching	washed
boxer	copiable	fitness	joys	players	sadly	study	washer
boxes	copying	fitting	joyful	plays	sadness	studying	washing
boys	could	forms	late	presses	safe	sturdy	were
brother	crashes	fox	lately	prewrap	safely	swimming	worlds
brotherly	cry	foxes	later	raged	served	tax	worry
brushes	crying	friendless	lighter	recopy	server	taxed	worrying
busy	define	fur	lighting	redefine	serving	taxes	would
busying	defining	furs	likeliest	refusal	she	thicker	wrap
buzz	defuse	fuse	madder	refused	shop	thickest	wrapper
buzzes	degrade	fuzz	maddest	related	shopped	thickly	write
buzzers	degrading	grader	madly	rented	shopping	thickness	writing
careful	delight	grading	madness	renter	shops	trap	wrong
carefully	delighting	happily	might	renting	signs	trappers	wrongly
careless	deserve	happiness	misfit	resorts	should	try	
carelessly	deserving	have	mother	rested	snapped	trial	

Section A Bases introduced in Lessons 47-56

stay	48	whether	49	loud	50	fact	53
deny	48	what	49	move	50	claim	53
did	48	when	49	woman	51	main	53
they	48	whole	49	cloud	51	file	53
fly	48	where	50	leave	51	vary	53
other	48	whose	50	neat	51	tract	53
come	49	sound	50	edit	51		
man	49	proud	50	act	53		

Section B Rules introduced in Lessons 47-56

Contractions (Lesson 47) "A contraction is made from two words, and a contraction has a part missing. We show that the part is missing with an apostrophe."

Section C Some words made from morphographs taught through Lesson 56

act	dried	fineness	invariable	nastily	runner	stopper	varied
armless	drier	finest	joyfully	nastiness	running	stopping	vary
bliss	driest	fly	leave	neat	sadden	sturdier	varying
busiest	drily	flying	leaving	neatly	saddest	sturdiest	we're
busier	drying	friendliest	lighter	other	sadness	sturdily	what
busily	duller	friendliness	loud	packing	she'll	swimmer	what's
business	edit	friendly	loneliest	pitied	shining	taking	when
carting	exacting	gradable	loneliness	pitiful	shopped	they	where
civilly	exchanges	grader	lonely	pitying	shopper	they'll	whether
claim	exclaim	grading	madden	played	shopping	thickest	whole
cloud	exports	happiest	maddest	player	signals	trappable	whose
contraction	express	happily	madness	playful	signers	trapper	widen
come	extract	happiness	main	playing	snapping	trapping	wideness
cried	fact	hated	man	proud	sound	trial	widest
defiling	fancied	hateful	matched	reacted	soundest	unmoved	woman
deniable	fancier	hater	misdeal	reclaimed	soundly	unrefillable	womanly
denied	fanciful	hating	mismatching	refreshed	soundness	unsound	worlds
deny	fancying	he'll	misspell	refusing	spell	unstops	you've
denying	file	hoped	movable	relight	stay	usable	
detract	filing	hopeful	move	removal	stayed	user	
did	filler	hoping	nastier	repressing	staying	using	
driable	finally	inexact	nastiest	resounded	stoppable	variable	

Appendix F

Section A Bases introduced in Lessons 57-64

please	57	thought	58	count	59	grow	61
ease	57	fame	58	found	59	show	61
spray	57	glory	58	very	59	feat	61
straight	57	fury	58	ruin	61		
about	57	text	59	fluid	61		
hole	57	place	59	under	61		

Section B Rules introduced in Lessons 57-64

Plural Variation (Lesson 57) "If a word ends in consonant-and-**y**, you add **es** to make the plural word."

Vowel-Consonant (Lesson 61) "If **w** is at the end of a morphograph, then it is a vowel letter."

Section C Some words made of morphographs taught through Lesson 65

about	cried	feat	hopelessly	mistaken	proverb	show	thoughtlessly
active	defaming	filing	hopelessness	misused	quietly	snapped	thoughtlessness
arms	deform	fluid	hotly	namable	raging	soundly	trial
babyish	delightful	flying	hotter	nastier	really	spray	uncivil
barest	denies	forceful	hottest	nastiest	refinable	stays	under
barred	depart	found	hurried	nastily	refined	stepped	unhappily
bars	depression	friendliness	hurrying	notable	relatively	stopping	unreal
bigger	deserving	friendly	inactive	notion	removal	straight	untried
boxing	designer	fury	inhuman	passage	renamed	straightened	usefully
brotherly	didn't	fusion	leaving	passion	rental	sturdier	using
busily	diner	glory	likable	place	repression	sturdiest	very
buzzes	driest	graded	likelihood	planner	reserved	sturdily	what's
cares	dropping	grow	lonelier	please	retraced	swimmer	widen
caring	ease	hasn't	loneliest	portable	retraction	text	widest
carriage	exclaim	hating	loudness	preserving	rightfully	they'll	wonderfully
cities	expressive	hole	madder	proclaimed	ruin	thought	worked
clannish	facing	hopeful	maddest	profiles	running	thoughtful	worldly
cloudiness	fact	hopefully	madly	profit	sadder	thoughtfully	worried
coming	fame	hopefulness	manly	profusely	served	thoughtfulness	
count	fanciful	hopeless	mainly	proudly	shopping	thoughtless	

226

Section A Bases introduced in Lessons 65-74

prove	65	side	66	pain	69	shape	71
poison	65	*ject*	66	brain	69	fry	71
blow	65	some	67	gain	69	physic	71
throw	65	out	67	sure	70	hero	72
cept	65	rich	67	cure	70	base	72
gress	65	sore	67	pure	70	prime	72
tect	65	shore	67	sent	70	tin	72
any	66	store	67	tent	70	spin	72
know	66	feet	67	graph	71	win	72
cause	66	give	69	phone	71	*tain*	72
pause	66	rain	69	photo	71		

Section B Some words made from morphographs taught through Lesson 74

any	give	poison	shape
base	given	preside	shiniest
blow	glorious	pressure	shiny
blower	graph	prime	shore
brain	happiest	primed	side
catchy	happily	procure	snappy
cause	happiness	progression	some
causing	hero	progressive	sore
cloudy	incurable	project	sorely
conception	injection	protection	spin
contain	inside	prove	spinning
contented	know	pure	store
cure	knowing	purely	sure
deceptive	lengthy	rain	surely
detained	maddest	rainy	tent
detective	madly	reception	texture
easier	madness	refried	throw
exception	nightly	regain	tin
famous	out	regress	undetectable
feet	outside	reinjected	uninsured
finely	pain	resent	unprotected
fineness	painfulness	reside	unproven
finest	pause	restore	widely
fried	phone	retain	wideness
fry	photo	retention	widest
furious	photograph	rich	win
fuzzy	physic	riches	winner
gain	physics	runny	
gainfully	pleasure	sent	

Appendix H

Section A Bases introduced in Lessons 75-83

quote	76	bet	77	state	78	first	81
quest	76	*pel*	77	spirit	79	thirst	81
quick	76	*vise*	78	chief	79	hop	81
quart	76	duty	78	niece	79	with	81
heavy	77	scope	78	grief	79	plant	81
breath	77	fail	78	brief	79	ship	81
head	77	rail	78	plain	80	tale	81
flat	77	tail	78	*duce*	80		

Section B Some words made from morphographs taught through Lesson 83

activists	failure	physicist	retailer
basics	first	plain	revise
bet	flat	plainly	revision
better	flatter	plant	scope
breath	flatly	planted	ship
breathlessness	friendless	planting	shipped
brief	friendliness	plants	shipping
briefly	glorious	produce	spirit
chief	gloriously	producing	spiritless
chiefly	graphics	propel	state
chiefs	grief	provisions	stately
conducive	head	quart	station
conquest	headed	quarter	stature
consent	headless	quest	studious
deduced	heaviest	question	studiously
detail	heavily	questionable	tail
devise	heavy	quick	tailing
disclaims	herbal	quicker	tale
discontented	heroic	quickly	thirst
discounted	hop	quotable	thirstiness
discounts	hopelessness	quote	thirsty
disease	hopped	racist	unheroic
disliked	hopping	rail	unrealistic
displace	induces	rails	unreduced
displeasing	inquest	realist	unrequested
displeasure	joyous	realistic	unrevised
disproves	joyously	receptionist	unstateliness
disquieting	misquoting	reduce	various
dispel	misstated	reducing	variously
duties	motorist	reinstate	vision
duty	nervous	relativist	with
expel	nervously	repel	without
explain	niece	request	
expressionist	nieces	requested	
fail	physical	retail	

Section A Bases introduced in Lessons 84-92

south	84	plane	85	get	88	cute	89
round	84	verse	85	road	88	athlete	89
cover	84	old	86	coat	88	muse	89
pound	84	hold	86	vote	88	magic	90
ground	84	bold	86	class	88	fashion	90
thousand	84	cold	86	sow	88	shake	90
danger	85	fold	86	cube	89	shed	90
chance	85	*fer*	86	huge	89	shout	90
		bid	88			*struct*	90

Section B Rules introduced in Lessons 84-92

En Variation (Lesson 87) "When the word ends with the letter **w,** and you add **en,** drop the **e.**"

Section C Some words made from morphographs taught through Lesson 92

athlete	construct	destructive	hugeness	outclassed	retain	sown	unathletic
athletic	constructively	detain	hugest	overcoats	reversal	structure	uncover
bid	contain	discovered	infer	overgrown	reverse	structuring	underground
blown	converse	fashion	instruct	overthrown	reversing	thousand	unfashionable
bold	conversely	fashionable	instructing	plane	road	thrown	unfold
boldness	conversion	fashioned	instruction	pound	round	transacted	unforgiving
chance	cover	fold	instructively	poundage	roundest	transaction	unfounded
chances	covering	folder	inverse	pounding	sew	transactional	unknown
chanciest	cube	forbid	inversely	prefer	sewn	transfer	unshakable
class	cubed	forget	inversion	push	shake	transformed	unshaken
classes	cubic	forgive	known	pushiness	shakes	transforming	unstructured
classier	cute	forgiven	magic	pushing	shakiness	transfuse	verse
classy	cutest	forgiveness	magical	pushy	shaking	transfusing	version
coat	danger	get	magically	railroad	shaky	transfusion	vote
cold	dangerous	getting	muse	recovery	shed	transgress	voter
coldest	defer	ground	music	refashioned	shedding	transgression	voting
coldly	define	grounded	musical	refer	shout	transplant	withhold
confer	deform	grown	musing	refine	shown	transplanted	withholding
confine	deplaned	hold	old	reform	south	transport	
conform	deserve	holding	olden	reserve	southerly	transporter	
conserve	destruction	huge	oldest	restructure	sow	transporting	

Appendix J

Section A Bases introduced in Lessons 93-106

logic	93	faint	95	broom	97	blot	99
part	93	wife	95	govern	98	bug	99
settle	93	loaf	95	cross	98	range	100
little	93	son	95	speech	98	mouth	100
ample	93	*fect*	96	sleep	98	long	100
middle	93	reach	96	sweet	98	came	100
four	93	speak	96	shelf	98	scribe	100
leaf	94	reason	96	sun	98	love	100
half	94	court	96	*cur*	98	join	101
thief	94	live	96	star	99	oil	101
wolf	94	life	96	rob	99	spoil	101
calf	94	fore	96	dim	99	major	101
self	94	choose	97	bed	99	test	101
tend	95	loose	97	hid	99	*mit*	101
type	95	soon	97	leg	99		
pose	95	cool	97	mud	99		
train	95	room	97	grab	99		

Section B Rules introduced in Lessons 93-106

AI Insertion (Lesson 95) "When the word ends in the letters **ic,** you must add the morphograph **al** before adding **ly**."

Plural Variation (Lesson 101) "Some words that end in the sound **fff** have the letters **ves** in the plural. You can always hear the sound **vvv** in the plural."

Section C Some words made from morphographs taught through Lesson 106

across	compartment	dejected	injected	magically	perfectionist	room	thieves
actual	compass	dejection	injection	major	performer	roomy	train
again	compassion	departure	instructional	manhood	permit	scribe	training
ahead	compel	describe	intended	middle	pertaining	self	transmit
alike	composer	dimness	intent	misspell	physically	selflessness	transpose
alive	compound	dispel	intention	motherhood	pose	settle	type
alone	compression	example	join	mouth	pretending	settlement	typically
ample	conceptual	exposure	joined	movement	project	shelf	unlovable
amused	concur	expression	leaf	musically	projected	shelves	unobtainable
amusement	confection	extending	leaves	object	projection	shipment	unreachable
apartment	confinement	factually	life	objected	range	sleep	unrealistically
around	conjoin	faint	lifelessness	objection	reach	son	unreasonable
aside	consignment	fainted	little	objectively	reached	soon	unselfish
basically	container	fore	littlest	oblong	realistically	sooner	unsettling
boyhood	contended	four	live	observable	reason	speak	unusual
breathtaking	context	govern	livelihood	obstruction	recur	speaker	usually
broom	contextual	government	living	obtained	reinforcement	speech	visually
brotherhood	cool	grabby	loaf	oil	rejoined	spoil	wife
calf	court	gradually	logic	ourselves	remit	spoiled	wives
calves	cross	graphically	logically	overextended	repel	statement	wolf
came	decomposable	half	long	part	repose	sun	wolves
choose	decompress	heroically	loose	parties	respell	sweet	yourself
choosy	defect	indescribable	loosened	partly	retyped	tend	yourselves
classically	defectiveness	induced	love	perception	robber	test	
commitment	deject	inject	loveliest	perfect	robbery	thief	

Section A Bases introduced in Lessons 107-112

merge	107	frog	107	family	108	shave	109
verge	107	trip	107	drive	108	knife	109
dress	107	ton	107	while	108	strain	109
just	107	gun	107	double	108	puff	109
critic	107	net	107	couple	108	gulf	109
vent	107	pig	107	trouble	108	*vert*	109
hit	107	rat	107	*sist*	108		
spot	107	chin	107	pretty	109		

Section B Some words made of morphographs taught through Lesson 112

alongside	detainment	knife	selfishly
aloud	double	knives	shave
amusement	doubly	lengthen	shelves
arise	dress	lifelong	statement
asleep	dressers	liveliness	straightened
athletically	dressiness	loaves	strain
atypically	drive	logically	strengthen
author	driver	magically	sturdiness
aversive	emit	merge	subhuman
became	equally	merger	subject
because	exposed	misbehaved	subjective
becoming	factual	musically	submerge
before	families	nervous	submit
befriend	family	objection	subscriber
behave	governing	observer	subside
beheaded	gradual	obstructively	subsist
belittle	grandson	obtained	subtract
belonging	graphically	overdrive	thieves
beloved	gulf	overextended	thoughtlessly
calves	gulfs	perceptive	transport
carrier	halves	perfectly	trouble
civilly	heroically	perform	troublesome
compound	impel	persist	unimpressed
conceptual	imported	physically	unimproved
consist	impose	portion	unjustly
constrained	impounded	prettily	unknown
content	impressionable	pretty	unquestionable
convention	impressively	prevent	unshaven
converge	improve	proportion	unspeakable
conversion	improvement	puff	unreachable
converted	impure	puffiness	unusually
coolly	incur	quarterly	vent
couple	indescribably	quietness	verge
critic	insisted	reasoning	whether
critically	intention	reception	while
decomposable	invent	relive	wives
decompression	invention	resisted	wolfish
defective	inverse	restraining	wolves
deserving	inverted	reversal	yourself
desist	just	reverted	yourselves

Appendix L

Section A Bases introduced in Lessons 113-123

hog	113	build	114	view	117	over	121
gas	113	lake	114	circle	117	value	121
car	113	script	114	*lent*	117	marry	121
pan	113	*ceive*	114	*plete*	117	set	122
bud	113	bought	115	*plore*	117	cap	122
top	113	fought	115	mote	118	up	122
gum	113	ought	115	speed	119	fog	122
cut	113	brought	115	screen	119	pop	122
red	113	day	115	freeze	119	bat	122
body	113	weak	115	*dict*	119	stir	122
wise	113	add	116	*cise*	120	tip	122
puzzle	113	sect	116	*fess*	120	sit	122
table	113	stance	116	*ceed*	120	dig	122
solve	113	*sume*	116	ready	121		
week	113	watch	117	point	121		
ply	114	science	117	beauty	121		

Section B Rules introduced in Lessons 113-123

Doubling Rule (Lesson 113) "When the word ends in a short **cvc** morphograph, use the doubling rule."

O-r Ending (Lesson 118) "Use **o-r** if a form of the word ends in **i-o-n**."

Section C Some words made of morphographs taught through Lesson 123

add	body	decisiveness	express	instance	preview	restoration	surrealistic
addict	bought	demote	expression	invaluable	primate	resume	surrounded
addiction	brought	deplete	expressive	lake	proceed	reviewer	table
address	build	deplorable	faction	leaves	professional	revision	tentative
adjust	building	depress	factor	marriage	professor	science	thieves
adjustment	circle	depression	factory	marry	promoted	screen	tractor
adventure	circling	description	formation	motion	promotion	screened	unaddressed
adventurer	commotion	designation	fought	motivate	protector	script	unadvised
adventuresome	complete	detector	freeze	notation	puzzle	scriptural	undiverted
adventurously	completely	devaluation	freezer	objector	puzzling	sect	uneventful
adverb	completion	dictation	friendship	ought	quotation	sections	uninformative
adversely	complying	dictatorship	graduation	outdistanced	readiness	setting	unrelenting
advise	compressor	diction	halves	over	ready	solve	unresolvable
applied	conceivable	digress	imploring	overcoat	received	speed	unsupported
attainable	conciseness	discovered	implying	overreacted	redesignate	speeding	valuable
attend	condense	dissect	impress	overview	referring	stance	value
attention	confess	dissolved	impression	plantation	relent	subscription	visor
attentiveness	confessor	distance	impressive	ply	relentless	substances	watch
attested	connotative	edict	inattentively	point	remote	supplant	weak
attraction	conscience	eject	incision	pointed	repelled	supply	weaknesses
attractive	consume	emerge	incomplete	precisely	replied	supportive	week
authorship	consumer	emitted	inconceivably	precision	reply	suppose	weekly
beautiful	conversation	emotion	inferring	predecessor	repress	supposed	wise
beauty	day	emotionless	information	predictable	repression	suppression	wisest
bodies	deceived	exploration	inscription	prediction	repressive	surface	wolves
bodily	decision	explore	insect	presumably	resolved	surname	

Section A Bases introduced in Lessons 124-140

merry	124	super	128	medic	131	stood	134
spire	124	mend	128	after	131	*pute*	134
sane	124	cave	128	break	131	ever	135
post	124	there	129	*mise*	131	nine	135
miss	124	scarce	130	*clude*	132	seven	135
cord	124	ideal	130	*vide*	132	quire	135
tour	125	grave	130	*gin*	132	got	135
dense	125	duct	130	air	133	sire	135
simple	125	*stant*	130	birth	133	*soci*	136
their	126	pare	130	ball	133	collar	136
cess	126	*trol*	130	noon	133	image	136
cern	126	lect	131	*pense*	133	*hilar*	136
rect	126	*turb*	131	teen	134		
tense	128	date	131	stand	134		

Section B Some words made of morphographs taught through Lesson 140

according	compensation	disputed	imagination	medic	procession	selective	tourists
accordion	compromise	disreputable	imagine	medically	product	service	transferred
acquire	computation	disturb	include	medicine	production	seven	unable
actor	computer	divide	indict	mend	productivity	seventeen	unamended
admission	concave	downward	indirectly	merry	promise	sideward	unbreakable
after	conceptualize	election	indispensable	miss	propeller	simple	uncivilized
afternoon	conclude	elective	individual	motorized	proverbial	simply	uncompromised
air	conductor	equalize	inexpensive	musician	provided	sociable	uncontrolled
airport	conferred	ever	inquire	nine	realism	social	understand
amend	conspired	every	inquiry	nineteen	realize	spiraling	understandably
amendment	contour	excess	insane	noon	recapped	spire	understood
aspiring	control	excessively	insanity	notice	recess	spiritual	undesirable
authorization	controller	excluding	insecurity	permission	recession	stand	undisturbed
authorized	cord	exhilarate	inspirational	perspire	recommended	standing	unforgettable
backward	criticism	expense	inspired	perturbed	record	stood	unindictable
ball	criticize	expensive	instantly	physician	recorder	submitted	unmanned
beginning	date	expensively	intensively	post	referred	substantial	unnoticed
birth	deduction	facial	intercepted	postage	repelled	super	unplanned
birthdate	dehumanizing	forbidden	interjection	poster	reputable	superhuman	unpredictable
break	dense	forgot	intermission	postscript	reputation	superimpose	unprepared
breaking	desirable	forgotten	intersect	precludes	required	supervise	unpreventable
cave	desire	forward	interview	predict	requirement	supervision	unproductive
cavity	detour	fourteen	introduce	predictable	sane	surrealism	unrecorded
civilian	dictate	got	introduction	prediction	sanitation	teen	unsnapped
collar	dictation	grave	invent	preferred	scarce	tense	unstoppable
commendable	dictator	gravity	invention	prepare	scarcely	tenseness	upwardly
commission	diction	hilarity	inventor	preparing	scarcity	tension	verbalize
committed	direct	humanity	justice	pretense	secluded	their	visualize
comparably	direction	ideal	logician	prevent	secure	there	withstand
compare	discern	ideally	magician	preventable	security	tour	
compelled	dispenser	image	majority	prevention	select	tourism	

Meanings of Non-word Bases, Prefixes, and Suffixes

Starred morphographs (*) may function either as words or as non-word bases.

Morphograph	Lesson	Meanings	Examples
a-	95	(in, on, at; not, without)	ahead, apart, atypical
-able	10	(able to be)	stretchable, washable, readable
ac-	125	(to, towards, against)	accept, account, access
act*	53	(to do, to drive)	actor, reaction, activate
ad-	114	(to, towards, against)	advise, adjustment, admitted
-age	28	(that which is; state)	usage, package, carriage
-al	30	(related to, like)	formal, structural, trial
ample*	93	(enough; to buy)	amply, examples
ap-	124	(to, towards, against)	appointment, approval, appendage
at-	119	(to, towards, against)	attract, attention, attest
-ate	122	(to make, act; having the quality of)	evaluate, activate, passionate
be-	107	(really; by; to make)	became, beside, because
ceed	120	(to go; to yield)	proceed, exceedingly, succeed
ceive	114	(to take; contain)	receiver, conceive, deceived
cent*	17	(hundred[th]; monetary unit; song; new)	percentage, century, recent
cept	65	(to take, contain)	receptive, intercept, acceptable
cern	126	(to perceive; to make certain)	concern, discerning
cess	126	(to go; to yield)	process, excessive, recession
cise	120	(to cut)	incision, concise, precisely
clude	132	(to close)	include, excluded, concluding
com-	97	(with, together; really)	compress, combat, commission
con-	40	(with, together; really)	conform, contest, condense
cord*	124	(rope; heart)	record, accord, cordial
cur*	98	(to run, to happen)	concur, recurred, current
cure*	70	(to heal; to care for)	curator, secure, inaccurate

234

de-	24	(away from, down, negative)	deport, depend, describe
di-	120	(away, negative; through, across)	divert, divide, direct
dict	119	(to speak; to fix)	predict, diction, addict
dis-	75	(away, apart; negative)	dispel, discount, disease
duce	80	(to lead)	produce, educate, reducing
duct*	130	(a pipe; to lead)	productive, conductor, deduction
e-	112	(out, away)	eject, event, emitted
-ed	15	(in the past; quality)	helped, uninformed, preferred
-en	27	(to make; in the past; quality of)	loosen, proven, golden
-er	18	(more; one who, that which)	easier, lighter, boxer
-es	38	(more than one; a verb marker for **he**, **she**, or **it**)	matches, boxes, carries
-est	4	(the most)	lightest, happiest, friendliest
ex-	53	(out, away)	export, exclude, extend
fact*	53	(reality; to do, to make)	factual, factory, factor
feat*	61	(doing something great; to do, to make)	defeat, feature
fect	96	(to do, to make)	defective, confection, perfect
fer	86	(to carry)	transfer, infer, referred
fess	120	(to speak)	profess, confession, professor
file*	53	(container; line, thread; foul)	filing, profile, defile
fine*	14	(high quality; thin; the end)	finest, final, infinite
fit*	41	(to suit; to do, to make)	outfit, profit, benefit
for-	89	(against, away)	forbid, forgotten, forgiving
found*	59	(find in the past; to base, to establish)	profound, founder, foundation
-ful	25	(full of)	careful, forgetful, beautiful
fuse*	37	(an electrical device; to pour or melt)	refuse, transfusion, confused
gin*	132	(to begin)	beginner

graph*	71	(chart; to write)	graphic, photograph, graphite
gress	65	(to step)	regression, progress, transgression
hilar	136	(merry)	exhilarate, hilarity, hilarious
-hood	100	(state, quality)	motherhood, likelihood, childhood
-ial	124	(related to, like)	partial, facial, adverbial
-ian	126	(one who)	magician, musician, civilian
-ic	80	(like, related to)	basic, typically, artistic
-ice	129	(act of; time of)	justice, service, notice
im-	108	(in, into; not)	impose, impression, impurity
in-	39	(in, into; not; really)	include, incurable, invaluable
-ine	133	(like, related to; feminine)	medicine, imagine, heroine
-ing	1	(when you do something; quality, state)	spending, moving, stopping
inter-	128	(between)	interact, intersect, intervention
intro-	127	(inside)	introduce, introvert, introduction
-ion	61	(state, quality, act)	action, taxation, repression
-ish	31	(like, related to; to make)	childish, selfish, finish
-ism	131	(state, quality; act)	tourism, criticism, realism
-ist	77	(one who)	artist, typist, tourist
-ite	126	(related to; quality, state, act)	composite, definite, cavity
-ive	59	(one who; quality of)	expressive, informative, relative
-ize	132	(to make more of something)	humanize, civilize, formalize
ject	66	(to throw)	rejecting, dejected, projection
late*	41	(after the usual time; to carry; wide)	translate, relation, dilate
lect	131	(to choose; to gather; to read)	select, elect, lecture
lent*	117	(slow)	relentless, lento
-less	6	(without)	painless, useless, restlessness
-ly	19	(how something is)	equally, basically, motherly
main*	53	(most important; to stay; hand)	mainland, remain, maintain

mend*	128	(to repair; fault)	amendment, commendable, recommendation
-ment	94	(that which; quality, act)	placement, requirement, apartment
merge*	107	(to unite; to dip, plunge)	merger, emerge, submerge
mis-	7	(wrong)	misspell, mistrial, misprint
mise	131	(to send)	demise, premise, promise
miss*	124	(fail to hit; to send)	admission, dismiss, missile
mit	101	(to send)	transmit, admitted, commitment
mote*	118	(to move)	motionless, demote, promotional
muse*	89	(one of the nine Muses)	amusement, bemused, musical
-ness	9	(that which is; state, quality)	thickness, thoughtfulness, uselessness
ob-	93	(to, toward, against; really)	obstruct, obtain, objection
-or	118	(one who, that which)	instructor, actor, factor
-ous	67	(having the quality of)	famous, furious, joyous
pare*	130	(to prepare; equal)	preparing, separate, compare
pass*	27	(to move on ahead; to suffer)	passage, passive, compassion
pel	77	(to push)	expel, propeller, repellent
pense	133	(to hang, to weigh; to pay)	expense, compensate, pension
per-	96	(through; really)	perform, pertain, perceive
plain*	80	(ordinary; flat; to lament)	complain, explainable, plaintive
plete	117	(full)	incomplete, deplete, repletion
plore	117	(to cry)	explore, implore, deplorable
ply*	114	(a layer; to fold; full)	pliable, comply, supplier
port*	4	(gate; to carry)	import, transportation, portable
pose*	95	(to act a certain way; to put, to place)	position, composure, opposite
post*	124	(the mail; an upright support; to place; after)	postage, poster, postscript
pound*	84	(16 oz.; monetary unit; to put, to place)	poundage, compound, expound

pre-	16	(before)	preview, preclude, predict
pro-	57	(in favor of; before; forward)	proclaim, provision, progress
prove*	65	(to test, to find good, to be useful)	proven, approval, improvement
pute	134	(to reckon)	computer, dispute, reputation
quart*	76	(four[th])	quarter, quarterly, quartet
quest*	76	(to seek, to ask for)	conquest, request, questionable
quire*	135	(to seek, to ask for)	acquire, required, inquiring
re-	1	(again, back; really)	rerun, return, repack
rect	126	(to rule; straight, right)	direct, resurrect, correct
-s	36	(more than one; a verb marker for **he**, **she**, or **it**)	parks, friends, designs
sane*	124	(of sound mind; healthy)	insane, sanitation, unsanitary
scribe*	100	(one who writes; to write)	describe, prescribe, subscriber
script*	114	(handwriting; to write)	descriptive, prescription, subscript
se-	133	(apart)	secluded, inseparable, selection
sect*	116	(a religious group; to cut)	section, dissect, intersect
sent*	70	(moved somewhere; to feel)	resentment, consent, dissent
serve*	16	(to give help; to save)	service, preserve, concervative
-ship	116	(state, quality)	friendship, hardship, relationship
side*	66	(one of the surfaces of an object; to sit)	alongside, preside, residual
sire*	135	(star)	desire, desirous
sist	108	(to stand, to set)	persist, resist, consists
soci	136	(companion)	sociable, association, socialize
sort*	4	(categorize; to go out)	assortment, consort, resort
spire*	124	(pointed tower; breath)	spiral, respiration, inspiring
stance*	116	(to stand, to set)	instance, substance, distance
stant	130	(to stand, to set)	constant, substantial, instant
struct	90	(to build)	structure, destruction, constructive

sub-	109	(under)	subtract, subhuman, submission
sume	116	(to take)	consumer, resume, presumably
sup-	117	(under)	support, suppressed, supposed
sur-	117	(under; over, above)	surname, surpass, surround
tail*	78	(the end; to cut)	detailed, retail, tailor
tain	72	(to hold)	retaining, container, detained
tect	65	(to cover)	detecting, protection
tend*	95	(to be inclined to; to stretch)	extend, attend, intend
tent*	70	(a portable shelter; to hold; to stretch)	retention, content, intently
test*	101	(exam; to witness)	attest, testify, testimony
text*	59	(written work; to weave)	textile, context, texture
tour*	125	(to visit; to turn)	tourist, detour, contour
tract*	53	(region; to drag, to draw)	tractor, attractive, subtraction
trans-	85	(across)	transportation, transform, transfer
trol	130	(regulate)	controller
turb	131	(to agitate)	perturb, disturb, turbulent
-ual	99	(related to, like)	factual, usual, gradual
un-	3	(not; reversal of)	unhappy, unusual, untie
-ure	65	(state, quality; that which)	departure, pressure, failure
vent*	107	(an outlet; to come)	prevent, invention, adventure
verb*	28	(oral, word)	verbal, adverb, verbalize
verge*	107	(the edge; to lean)	converge, diverge
verse*	85	(a line of poetry; to turn)	conversation, reversal, versatile
vert	109	(to turn)	invert, convert, introvert
vide	132	(to see; to separate)	providing, divide, individual
vise*	78	(clamp; to see; to separate)	advise, visual, division
-ward	133	(toward)	backward, homewards, outwardly
-y	70	(having the quality of; in the manner of; small)	shiny, activity, doggy

Five-Lesson Point Summaries

1.

Lesson	1	2	3	4	5	Total
Points						

2.

Lesson	6	7	8	9	10	Total
Points						

3.

Lesson	11	12	13	14	15	Total
Points						

4.

Lesson	16	17	18	19	20	Total
Points						

5.

Lesson	21	22	23	24	25	Total
Points						

6.

Lesson	26	27	28	29	30	Total
Points						

7.

Lesson	31	32	33	34	35	Total
Points						

8.

Lesson	36	37	38	39	40	Total
Points						

9.

Lesson	41	42	43	44	45	Total
Points						

10.

Lesson	46	47	48	49	50	Total
Points						

11.

Lesson	51	52	53	54	55	Total
Points						

12.

Lesson	56	57	58	59	60	Total
Points						

13.

Lesson	61	62	63	64	65	Total
Points						

14.

Lesson	66	67	68	69	70	Total
Points						

Five Lesson Point Summary Chart

15.

Lesson	71	72	73	74	75	Total
Points						

16.

Lesson	76	77	78	79	80	Total
Points						

17.

Lesson	81	82	83	84	85	Total
Points						

18.

Lesson	86	87	88	89	90	Total
Points						

19.

Lesson	91	92	93	94	95	Total
Points						

20.

Lesson	96	97	98	99	100	Total
Points						

21.

Lesson	101	102	103	104	105	Total
Points						

22.

Lesson	106	107	108	109	110	Total
Points						

23.

Lesson	111	112	113	114	115	Total
Points						

24.

Lesson	116	117	118	119	120	Total
Points						

25.

Lesson	121	122	123	124	125	Total
Points						

26.

Lesson	126	127	128	129	130	Total
Points						

27.

Lesson	131	132	133	134	135	Total
Points						

28.

Lesson	136	137	138	139	140	Total
Points						

Five-Lesson Summary Chart

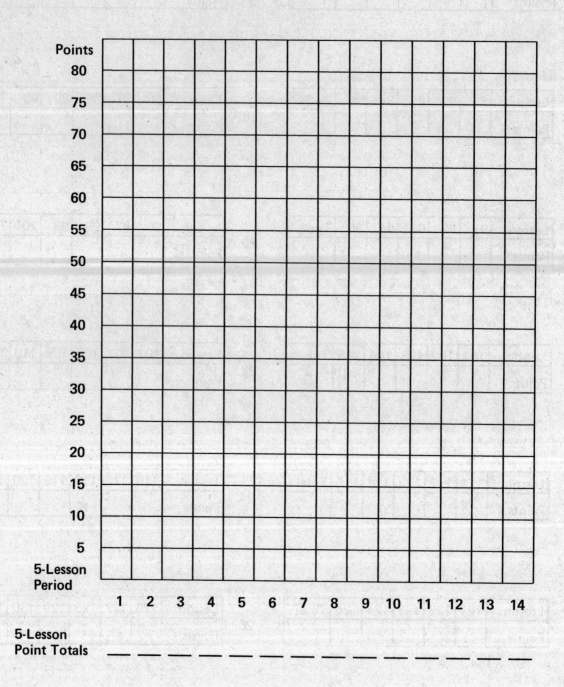

Points

5-Lesson Period

5-Lesson Point Totals — — — — — — — — — — — — — —

Five–Lesson Summary Chart

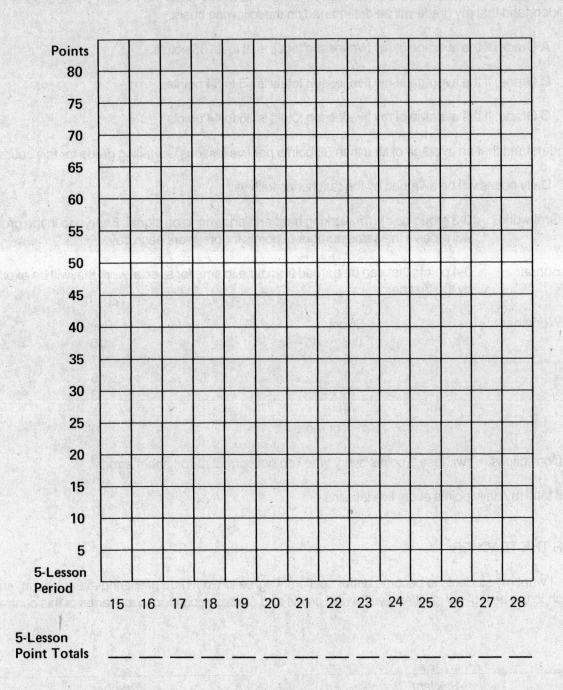

Points

80
75
70
65
60
55
50
45
40
35
30
25
20
15
10
5

5-Lesson
Period

15 16 17 18 19 20 21 22 23 24 25 26 27 28

5-Lesson
Point Totals __ __ __ __ __ __ __ __ __ __ __ __ __ __

CONTRACT

Corrective Spelling

FOR THE STUDENT:

I want to become a better speller. I agree to work hard and follow the teacher's instructions. I understand that my grade will be determined on the following basis:

A Grade: If the average of my five-lesson totals is at least 55 points.

B Grade: If the average of my five-lesson totals is 45 to 54 points.

C Grade: If the average of my five-lesson totals is 35 to 44 points.

I understand that an average of less than 35 points per five lessons is a failing grade for this course.

Daily points will be awarded by the teacher as follows:

1. Oral work   0-3 group points for working hard and answering on signal. Everyone in the group will receive the same number of points for oral work each day.

2. Bonus   0-4 points that can be earned from time to time for special work that will be explained by the teacher.

3. Worksheet

Errors	Points
0-2	10
3	7
4	5
5	3
6	1
7 or more	0

4. Corrections: I will lose 3 points every time I do not correct a worksheet error.

I will total my daily points every five lessons.

FOR THE TEACHER:

I want my students to become better spellers. I agree to work hard preparing every lesson, and to teach to the best of my abilities. I will award points and grades according to the terms of this contract.

_____   _____
           Student   *Teacher*